Exploring Virginia's Human Resources

# Exploring Virginia's Human Resources

Edited by Roscoe D. Hughes

and Henry Lcidheiser, Jr.

The University Press of Virginia

Charlottesville

# Acknowledgments

THE essays in this volume are based on papers presented at a symposium sponsored by the Virginia Academy of Science in May 1964, with the generous support and cooperation of the Virginia Chamber of Commerce. We, the members of the Symposium Committee, gratefully acknowledge our indebtedness to the following: Jackson J. Taylor, president of the Virginia Academy of Science in 1961–62, for initiating plans for the symposium; Foley F. Smith, president of the Virginia Academy of Science in 1962–63, for lending his good offices to facilitate it; Verbon E. Kemp, executive director, and James T. Mathews, president of the Virginia Chamber of Commerce in 1963–64, for their many helpful suggestions in planning the symposium and their willingness to support a project having potential importance not only to commerce and business in Virginia but also to government, science, and labor; Richard S. Gillis, present executive secretary of the Chamber of Commerce, and his staff for their efficient handling of symposium matters; and last but not least Thomas C. Boushall, chairman of the board, The Bank of Virginia, for his enthusiastic support and unflagging interest in this undertaking from its inception.

Symposium Committee

Roscoe D. Hughes, Chairman
Henry Leidheiser, Jr., Cochairman
Edward W. Gregory, Jr.
Lorin A. Thompson

# Contents

# Illustrations and Tables

## MAPS

## FIGURES

## TABLES

# Introduction

# Introduction

*Roscoe D. Hughes, Chairman*

*Department of Biology and Genetics*

*Medical College of Virginia*

*and*

*Henry Leidheiser, Jr., Director,*

*Virginia Institute for Scientific Research*

Virginia is blessed with abundant natural resources. Her beautiful mountains, their ruggedness softened by the hands of time, are one of these. Beneath their tree-covered slopes often lie deposits of coal and other minerals. Between these mountains—the Shenandoah, Blue Ridge, Allegheny, and Appalachian, which Virginia shares with her neighbors —nestle the valleys, whose rich soil supports a thriving agricultural economy of immense orchards and fine herds of cattle. The foothills and plains of the Piedmont are found to the east. Its ample forests and minerals support many industries, small and large; its soil and climate are the basis of thriving farming communities. Farther to the east is Tidewater Virginia, where the waters of the Rappahannock, the York, the James, and the Potomac reach the level of the sea. Its rivers and bays give the Tidewater region ready access to the commerce of the world. Its many inlets and estuaries provide harbors for thousands of pleasure craft. Its marine life makes the Chesapeake Bay one of the richest bodies of water in the world. The shining beaches of its coast line bring innumerable vacationers each year. Its heavy industry, including shipbuilding, supports a high concentration of people which places it in the urban corridor of the East Coast of the United States. The extent of Virginia's natural resources is well documented and was recently the subject of a symposium sponsored by the Virginia Academy of Science and the Virginia Institute for Scientific Research.[1]

Another great resource of Virginia, a resource that does not diminish with use, is its cultural and political heritage. This may take the form of a structure, for example, Jefferson's Capitol; or an institution, for example, Jefferson's University. More likely it is an idea—or an ideal—for example, Jeffersonian democracy. Perhaps it is the tradition of modesty, moderation, and good taste of its people. Whatever it is, it helps shape the lives of Virginians in and out of their state.

But a state's, or a nation's, greatest resource is its people. Today Virginia has a population of 4,200,000. How does one assess the productivity and creativity of these people? The essays comprising this volume will attempt to make such an assessment. Fundamentally this is

---

[1] "Symposium on Basic Research on Virginia's Natural Resources," *Virginia Journal of Science*, XIII (1962), 67–94.

accomplished by examining the changing structure, or composition, of the population of the state. Although it would be intriguing and possibly fruitful to attempt to assess the influence of certain individuals on the productivity and creativity of Virginia's people, this is not the purpose of this volume. Nor is this volume primarily concerned with institutions, facilities, or agencies, although, for example, the health of Virginians obviously cannot be separated from health agencies and the education of Virginians from educational institutions.

The first two essays deal all too briefly with Virginia's people during the seventeenth, eighteenth, and nineteenth centuries. What were the early settlers like? What were their national and racial origins? Were they adventurers or were they the oppressed? These original settlers, the people of many lands who continued to migrate to Virginia in the decades that followed, and, of course, the influx of people from other states of the Union were the progenitors of Virginia's population today. An understanding of Virginia's people and the factors contributing to their distinctiveness can best be gained through the historical perspective given by these essays.

The search for an environment compatible with the economic ambitions and cultural proclivities of individuals and groups may, and often does, lead to frequent and widespread changes of residence. Urbanization finds Virginia a typical exponent of this national phenomenon. The cityward trends in Virginia, with hints of their momentous social and economic implications, are presented in the third essay.

Scientific and technological advances since the turn of the century have been so great and so encompassing that they have taken us literally from the horse-and-buggy age to the nuclear age; one of our national goals is now to send Americans to the moon by the end of this decade. One of the many consequences of these advances is overproduction on the farm and migration to the city of workers untrained in manufacturing and commercial trades. So rapid have been the technological changes in recent times that the training and education of skilled workers have been thrown out of balance with the needs. The problem has been and is receiving attention at the highest state and federal governmental levels. Essays 4 and 5 outline the constantly changing state of training and education of blue-and white-collar workers and the need for specialized skills and qualifications among our people.

The structural characteristics of Virginia's population of tomorrow are being largely determined by the reproductive patterns of Virginia's people today. Essay 6 discusses population growth in Virginia and shows that while Virginia's people are unquestionably its greatest resource, the present and projected reproductive rate among all of its economic groups is not an unmixed blessing. Could it be that mere numbers of people are not enough? Perhaps Virginia's contribution to society will be judged in the future as in the past by the quality of its people. If so, differential reproduction is an essentially modern problem that must be studied and carefully weighed.

In the seventh and eighth essays the physical and mental health of Virginians is explored. Both presentations compare health statistics of Virginia with those of other states and of the nation as a whole. There is much in these statistics that Virginians can point to with pride. Yet it is an area in which our knowledge is not great enough to enable us to make immense strides toward improvement. No other characteristic of the people is more obviously related to productivity than their physical and mental health; no other characteristic so obviously contributes to the resources of an individual or a population.

In the last essay the difficult task of assessing the mental aptitudes and talents of Virginia's people is attempted. Is Virginia still producing the great leaders, the mental giants, it did in former years? If so, are they migrating to other states where their talents can be better utilized?

It can be argued that since the characteristics and qualities of the people of the United States as a whole represent a continuum, it is artificial, if not meaningless, to attempt an analysis of one segment of this continuum—the area within the boundaries of Virginia. However, so many decisions that affect the attributes of the people are still made at the state level, even in this period of growing federal dominance, that state populations can be shown to be qualitatively different if suitable parameters are used. It follows then that if the right decisions affecting or relating to Virginia's human resources are to be made by any agency of the government, or by business or industry, greater knowledge of our people must be available.

The purpose of this volume will not be achieved simply by bringing together discerning analyses of Virginia's people today as seen in a number of aspects. Only if these analyses focus the attention of government, industry, and science on the need for continuing research on, and for the development of measures to improve, Virginia's human resources will the contributors be satisfied.

1

# Virginia's First Families and the First Families of Virginia

*Wilcomb E. Washburn*

*Curator, Division of Political History*

*Smithsonian Institution*

*Washington, D.C.*

In his essay "Of Plantations" Francis Bacon wrote: "Planting of countries is like planting of woods; for you must make account to lose almost twenty years' profit, and expect your recompense in the end: for the principal thing that hath been the destruction of most plantations hath been the base and hasty drawing of profit in the first years."[1] The establishment of the Virginia colony is a classic illustration of Bacon's axiom. Thousands of settlers went to Virginia in the early years after its founding in 1607, but few survived. John Smith estimated that 7,000 colonists died between 1607 and 1624, leaving 1,500 survivors.[2] His estimates have, in general, been accepted by later authorities.[3] A careful census taken in 1624 showed a total population for the colony of 1,232, of whom 940 were white males, 12 were Negro males, 269 were white females, and 11 Negro females.[4] It seems clear that disease was the great killer despite the loss of 347 persons in the Indian massacre of 1622 and the return of some to England in disappointment.

What can explain this early, almost incredible death rate, a rate that was not limited to Virginia? The Plymouth Colony, for example, lost half of its 100 settlers in the first year, as did the Jamestown settlement.[5] No one knows the answer, and it provides a challenge to an enterprising medical researcher or medical historian. Numerous theories exist, most of which refer to the environmental conditions at Jamestown as the breeder of the killing agents.[6] I sometimes wonder whether the whites lacked immunity to certain diseases carried by the Indians just as the

[1] *The Essays, or Councels, Civil and Moral*, ed. Samuel Harvey Reynolds (Oxford, 1890), p. 237.

[2] *Travels and Works*, ed. Edward Arber and A. G. Bradley (Edinburgh, 1910), II, 884.

[3] Introduction by Earl G. Swem to *Adventurers of Purse and Person: Virginia, 1607–1625*, comp. and ed. Annie Lash Jester, in collaboration with Martha Woodroof Hiden (sponsored by the Order of the First Families of Virginia, 1607–1620; [Princeton?, N.J.] 1956), p. xv; Wesley Frank Craven, *The Southern Colonies in the Seventeenth Century, 1607–1689* (Baton Rouge, La., 1949), p. 147; Alexander Brown, *The First Republic in America* (Boston, 1898), p. 612.

[4] *Virginia Magazine of History and Biography*, VII (1899–1900), 364–65.

[5] Samuel H. Yonge, "The Site of Old 'James Towne,' 1607–1698," *Va. Mag. Hist. Biog.*, XI (1903–4), 400; Edward Channing, *A History of the United States*, vol. I, *The Planting of a Nation in the New World, 1000–1660* (New York, 1905, repr. 1948), 307–8.

[6] Thomas P. Hughes wrote a compact account of *Medicine in Virginia, 1607–1699*, which was published as one of the Jamestown 350th Anniversary Historical Booklets by the Virginia 350th Anniversary Celebration Corporation (Williamsburg, Va., 1957).

latter lacked immunity to European diseases such as smallpox and measles. The Indians were decimated by European diseases. Is it possible that the Europeans had to build up an immunity to Indian diseases? Governor Sir William Berkeley, writing in 1671 in response to a request from the lords of Trade and Plantations for information on various facets of Virginia life, including the death rate, wrote:

All new plantations are, for an age or two, unhealthy, 'till they are thoroughly cleared of wood; but unless we had a particular register office, for the denoting of all that died, I cannot give a particular answer to this query, only this I say, that there is not often unseasoned hands (as we term them) that die now, whereas heretofore, not one of five escaped the first year.[7]

Berkeley's observation is borne out by the rapid growth of the colony in the period following 1625. In a report to the king of March 26, 1628, the governor, Council, and Burgesses reported that the colony consisted of "near three thousand persons, or shortly being likely to attain that number."[8] Governor Sir John Harvey on May 29, 1630, reported to the Privy Council that he had not had time to take a census of the people but he estimated them to number upward of 2,500.[9] Despite heavy immigration, the key to the increase was probably in the increasing immunity to whatever diseases were present and in the growing numbers of women in the colony. As Berkeley wrote in *A Discourse and View of Virginia* while in England in 1662, the early settlement contained "not one woman to thirty men, and *populus virorum* is of no long duration anywhere."[10]

By 1640 the population had reached about 8,000.[11] By 1649, when the pamphlet *A Perfect Description of Virginia* was published in London, the total population of Virginia was estimated at "about fifteen thousand English, and of negroes brought thither, three hundred good servants."[12]

In 1671, when Governor Berkeley returned his answers to the inquiries of the lords of Trade, he estimated that Virginia had 40,000 persons—men, women, and children—of whom 2,000 were "black slaves," 6,000 Christian servants "for a short time, the rest are born in the country or have come in to settle and seat, in bettering their condition in a growing country." Berkeley estimated the yearly flow of servants into the colony at about 1,500 "of which, most are English, few Scotch, and fewer Irish, and not above two or three ships of negroes in seven years."[13]

---

[7] William W. Hening, ed., *The Statutes at Large . . . A Collection of All the Laws of Virginia* (Richmond [etc.], 1819–23), II, 515.

[8] *Va. Mag. Hist. Biog.*, VII (1899–1900), 262.     [9] *Ibid.*, 381.

[10] London, 1663 (reproduced in facsimile, Norwalk, Conn., 1914), p. 3.

[11] Craven, *op. cit.*, p. 177.

[12] Reprinted in *Virginia Historical Register, and Literary Advertiser*, ed. William Maxwell, II (1849), 62.     [13] Hening, *op. cit.*, II, 515.

By the end of the century the total number of "souls," according to the Census List for 1703, was 60,606, of whom 25,023 were tithables and 35,583 women and children. Robert Beverley, in giving the figures in *The History and Present State of Virginia,* published in London in 1705, explained that "they call all Negroes above sixteen years of Age Tithable, be they Male or Female; and all white men of the same age. But Children and white Women, are exempted from all manner of Duties."[14]

Historians give varying reasons for the initially slow but later rapid growth of the colony. These reasons include the efficiency, or lack of it, of the company which managed the colony until 1624; the benevolence, or lack of it, of the Crown, which took over the colony and appointed a royal governor in the following year; the virtue, or lack of it, of the individual colonists; the severity, or lack of it, of the several governors; and so on. It is not possible to examine all these factors in detail here.

While the colony was under the management of the Virginia Company, a joint-stock venture in which individual or corporate investors in England in the expectation of monetary reward invested money, sent colonists, or did both, the colony barely managed to sustain itself. Indeed, at one point the remaining colonists actually got into their ships and started down the James River to return to England but were turned around by the arrival of a new governor and fresh supplies. The leadership, in the earliest years, was not clear-cut. Later this defect was remedied and authority was defined with military precision. Throughout this period the colony was not an aggregate of individuals working for themselves, but a corporate venture undertaken by members and servants of the company, who were restricted in various ways from engaging in individual enterprise in trade and land purchase.

Gradually the private interest was accorded increasing recognition, both through the allocation of limited allotments of private land and by the creation, in 1619, of an assembly of representatives of the separate settlements to help form the laws under which the colony was to be run. It should be kept in mind that settlements in the early years of the seventeenth century were compact, organized communities, not scattered individual plantations as in the latter part of the century. The locations of these compact "particular plantations" and settlements are recorded in one of the Jamestown 350th Anniversary Celebration Corporation booklets, that by Charles F. Hatch, Jr.[15]

Despite the introduction of a representative assembly in 1619, the reins of government were more tightly held on the individual colonist in

[14] Ed. Louis B. Wright (Chapel Hill, N.C., 1947), p. 252.
[15] *The First Seventeen Years, Virginia, 1607–1624* (Williamsburg, Va., 1957).

the early years of the settlement than is sometimes realized. Although the colony ceased to be run in a military fashion, Virginia governors both possessed and exercised great power as the supreme civil and military representative of the king's majesty in the colony. Virginia governors of the seventeenth century are, moreover, distinguished by the quality of personal leadership. The names of Captain John Smith (during the period of company control), Sir John Harvey, and Sir William Berkeley stand out as governors who personally captured Indian chiefs, who cudgeled obstreperous councilors, and who dismissed panicky and misinformed petitioners with contempt. Their actions are regarded by later observers as *prima-facie* evidence of their antidemocratic bias. This view misses the point. You cannot compare a seventeenth-century governor and a twentieth-century governor. Sir William Berkeley and Terry Sanford (governor of North Carolina, 1961–4) — to take one recent example — were both good men, but they cannot be compared. They functioned in societies which differed too greatly.

It is hard for us in the twentieth century to visualize the web of relationships and responsibilities that bound the seventeenth-century man to his fellows and to his God and king. This semifeudal web, which is to us so restrictive and so much in violation of our cherished individual freedom, was as accepted a part of the social fabric of the seventeenth century as individual freedom is a part of twentieth-century philosophy. Not that the feudal philosophy had not been called into question: it had, and it was being destroyed or eroded throughout the period. The seventeenth century was the great period of transition of modern times. The science of Newton, the psychology of Locke, the philosophy of Hobbes — all helped to pull England, and by extension the American colonies, into the modern age. But tradition is not so easily dispensed with, and the birth pangs of the new age were long and hard.

The governors of Virginia in the first three quarters of the seventeenth century did not interpret the welfare of the colony to be the sum total of the welfare of the individuals constituting that society. They did assume that one of the purposes of the state was to further the welfare of the people, but they did not assume that the individual subject was the proper judge of what constituted his own individual welfare, or the welfare of the state. They conceived, furthermore, that the state had a being and welfare of its own, which could often be furthered only by the sacrifice of the welfare of the individual. This attitude was expressed characteristically and pungently by Berkeley in *A Discourse and View of Virginia* when he affirmed "that never any Community of people had good done to them, but against their wills."[16]

Berkeley's constant efforts to use the state as an agency of social

[16] P. 8.

control—to use it economically to free Virginia from dependence upon tobacco and to encourage instead, by the importation of skilled craftsmen in various fields, a diversified and industrialized economy—evince this attitude. Even the phrase "community of people," as used by Berkeley, is significant. The governor thought not in terms of individuals, but in terms of a community.

Despite the orientation of the governors to the quasi-feudal society they were bound to uphold, the revolution toward what one writer has called a "possessive market society" continued, both in Virginia and in Europe, under the impact of economic forces seen most clearly by philosophers such as Thomas Hobbes. "By possessive market society," writes C. B. Macpherson, the author responsible for the phrase,

I mean one in which, in contrast to a society based on custom and status, there is no authoritative allocation of work or rewards, and in which, in contrast to a society of independent producers who exchange only their produce in the market, there is a market in labour as well as in products. If a single criterion of the possessive market society is wanted it is that man's labour is a commodity, i.e. that a man's energy and skill are his own, yet are regarded not as integral parts of his personality, but as possessions, the use and disposal of which he is free to hand over to others for a price.[17]

It is not possible, in the brief confines of this paper, to apply the theory fully to Virginia, but suffice it to say that Virginia's economy and society in the seventeenth century can be said to be evolving, as were those of Europe generally, from a status society to one based on the demands of the possessive market.

Of critical importance in causing this shift were the abandonment of the quantitative restrictions on purchase of land incorporated in the "headright" system and the introduction of a pure market freedom in the purchase of this commodity in the last decade of the century.[18] While the headright continued to be utilized along with the new "treasury right," the ratio of man to land in Virginia was no longer tied in a rough proportion of fifty acres a man, as it had been under the headright system alone. It is important to remember that, despite the growing proportion of births in the colony, land was still easily available at the end of the century under the headright system because the high death rate, lapsed land, and other causes put once-patented land back on the market. As Robert Beverley put it, in 1705, "Each Servant at his Freedom . . . has then also a Right to take up fifty Acres of Land, where he can find any unpatented: But that is no great Privilege, for any one may have as good a right for a piece of Eight." "These Rights to Land,"

[17] *The Political Theory of Possessive Individualism: Hobbes to Locke* (Oxford, 1962), p. 48, printed by permission of the Clarendon Press.
[18] Richard L. Morton, *Colonial Virginia* (Chapel Hill, N.C., 1960), I, 362, II, 539.

Beverley went on, "are as commonly sold by one Man to another, as the Land it self; so that any one, not having Rights by his own Importation, may have them by Purchase."[19] Nevertheless, the addition of a simple treasury right system by which land could be purchased for money alone laid the basis for a fundamental alteration in Virginia society. Man was no longer tied to land in a fixed ratio.

In the same way, the increasingly significant market in labor—slave labor—can be said to have caused a shift in another fundamental element in the economy impelling it more rapidly toward a possessive market society. In a society in which slavery is already established and is not increasing appreciably in numbers, such a labor system can be an element of social stability; but in a society which is literally purchasing a new labor supply at the same time that it is suddenly purchasing a new land supply, both land and labor are reckoned in terms of individual cost rather than in terms of societal cohesion or human dignity. The sudden rise in importations of Negroes in the latter part of the seventeenth century, coincidental with the introduction of a system of unlimited purchase of land for money alone, is an economic and social revolution unparalleled in the history of any society, and as yet its effects have not been fully appreciated.

In another paper I have suggested that Bacon's Rebellion, which shred the fabric of Virginia society in 1676, can be said to punctuate the shift from a status society to one based on possessive individualism.[20] The rebellion and its aftermath marked the loss of political control by Governor Berkeley and his followers, who sought to maintain the traditional social controls of a status society, and it heralded the introduction of a possessive market society governed by individual power and profit. The Council of State in Virginia in the seventeenth century constituted a sensitive barometer of this movement. Its members were torn between their responsibility to maintain the social fabric of the quasi-feudal state and their opportunities to enhance their individual well-being through land acquisition and the sale of tobacco. In the inevitable divisions that occur in any state and in any government the Council was sometimes for and sometimes against the governor. Increasingly the concept of a higher loyalty to the state faded. In the period of Bacon's Rebellion a number of the Council members cooperated with the rebels. With the mismanagement following the rebellion the Council increasingly washed its hands of loyalty to a remote and

[19] *Op. cit.*, pp. 274, 277; see also Robert E. Brown and B. Katherine Brown, *Virginia, 1705–1786: Democracy or Aristocracy?* (East Lansing, Mich., 1964), p. 11.
[20] "Law and Authority in Colonial Virginia," in George A. Billias, ed., *Law and Authority in Colonial America* (Barre, Mass., 1965), pp. 116–138. See also Wilcomb E. Washburn, "The Effect of Bacon's Rebellion on Government in England and Virginia," in Smithsonian Institution, *Contributions from the Museum of History and Technology, United States National Museum*, Bull. 225 (1962), paper 17.

inefficient English government and sided more and more with the Burgesses and the planters in promoting their individual interests against that of the Crown.[21]

I have come this far and have discoursed to some degree on Virginia's first families, but have not indicated how they may differ—if, in fact, they do—from the First Families of Virginia.

Historians of the present day, as did critics in England at the time, have asserted that the colony of Virginia was, in the words of the seventeenth-century English clergyman Samuel Purchas, "much encombered with Englands excrements" and "made a Port Exquiline for such as by ordure or vomit were by good order and physicke worthy to be evacuated from This Body."[22] No better answer can be given to the charge today than was given by Sir William Berkeley 302 years ago:

An other great imputation lyes on the Countrey [he wrote] that none but those of the meanest quality and corruptest lives go thither. This to our Maligners we would easily grant, if they would consent to the *omen* of it; for was not *Rome* thus begun and composed? and the great honour that was given to *Romulus* and his City was this, that his severity and discipline in his time, made them formidable to their neighbours, and his posterity masters of the world. But this is not all truth, for men of as good Families as any Subjects in England have resided there, as the *Percys*, the *Barkleys*, the *Wests*, the *Gages*, the *Throgmortons, Wyats, Degges, Chickeleys, Moldsworths, Morrisons, Kemps*, and hundred others, which I forbear to name, lest I should misherald them in the Catalogue.[23]

Berkeley asserted that, whether considered "experimentally or morally," the plantations changed dissolute and prodigal younger sons of the English gentry into provident and industrious Virginia landowners and heads of households. The knowledge that hard work would be rewarded with prosperity in the colonies, asserted Berkeley, "makes men industrious and vigilant with us, who here [in England] having no Vineyards to dresse, stood idle in the Market-place till the eleventh hour."[24] That the eldest sons, those who inherited their father's titles and lands in England, did not emigrate to the colonies should be no cause for surprise, since their position and their wealth depended upon their staying in England. However, that the younger sons of England could in effect become elder sons by transporting themselves to a realm in which new land could be had on easy terms has not been sufficiently appreciated.

Of the utmost significance is the fact that while the Virginia colony began its early years with a large majority of servants in proportion to the total population, similar to the proportions in England itself, as the

---

[21] Jack P. Greene, *The Quest for Power: The Lower Houses of Assembly in the Southern Royal Colonies, 1689–1776* (Chapel Hill, N.C., 1963).
[22] *Hakluytus Posthumus; or, Purchas IIis Pilgrimes* (Glasgow, 1905–7), XIX, 236.
[23] *Op. cit.*, p. 3.      [24] *Ibid.*, p. 4.

seventeenth century wore on the upgrading process that Berkeley so perceptively described had its effect, and by the end of the century only a small minority of the white population were servants, in contrast to the situation in England.[25] Berkeley hoped that the newly endowed colonist, with land and labor at his disposal, elevated to a new dignity, would remain loyal to the principles of a society oriented to nonindividualistic ends. He was doomed to be disappointed. The economic and social revolution was too complete, and the incapacity of the English government to realign the political bonds between mother country and colony spelled ultimate separation.

The principal modern statement of the anticavalier tradition is given by Thomas Jefferson Wertenbaker, whose *Patrician and Plebeian in Virginia; or, The Origin and Development of the Social Classes of the Old Dominion* was published in Charlottesville by the author in 1910. In his preface to the 1910 edition (omitted in the 1958 and 1959 reprints), Wertenbaker asserted that

it was for many years the general belief that the leading planters were the descendants of English families of high rank, and that their aristocratic instincts were their birth-right, the heritage left them by noble ancestors. . . . The Author's own studies have led him to the conclusion that but few men of rank ever came to the "wilderness of Virginia," and that the planters were in most cases the descendants of merchant ancestors.[26]

It is easy, of course, to demolish any number of straw men that one might set up about Virginia immigration, whether it be Dr. Samuel Johnson's charge that the Americans were a race of convicts, an assertion which Wertenbaker, in the preface to his reprint of *Patrician and Plebeian,* feels impelled to refute, or the "old belief that the Virginia aristocracy had its origin in a migration of Cavaliers after the defeat of the royalists in the British Civil War," which Wertenbaker's book was designed to demolish.[27]

But the historian should not glory in easy victories over obviously uninformed and ill-prepared opponents. Rather, to carry over into a different context the admonition of Robert E. and B. Katherine Brown in

25 The reviewer of Thomas Jefferson Wertenbaker's *Patrician and Plebeian* in the *Va. Mag. Hist. Biog.* (XVIII [1910], 344–45) estimated that 15 percent were servants in 1671 as opposed to 60 percent in 1637. For the English figures, see Gregory King's estimates for 1688, reprinted as an appendix to Macpherson, *op. cit.*, pp. 279–92.

26 Nowhere in the book does Wertenbaker notice or answer the arguments of Sir William Berkeley quoted above. In 1946 John E. Manahan presented a doctoral thesis to the University of Virginia entitled "The Cavalier Remounted: A Study of the Origins of Virginia's Population, 1607–1700," in which he attempts to refute Wertenbaker's thesis. For a significant recent study, see Bernard Bailyn, "Politics and Social Structure in Virginia," in James Morton Smith, ed., *Seventeenth-Century America: Essays in Colonial History* (Chapel Hill, N.C., 1959), pp. 90–115.

27 *Patrician and Plebeian,* reprinted in *The Shaping of Colonial Virginia* (New York, 1958) and separately (New York, 1959), pp. i, vi.

their study of democracy and aristocracy in eighteenth-century Virginia:

The problem is not so much whether there were different "classes," which can be accepted as an axiom, but to determine their nature and their relation to each other. What was the relative size of the distinguishable classes, and was the social structure rigid or was there sufficient fluidity to allow much social mobility?[28]

The problem in analyzing social classes of the seventeenth century is not only to count the number of convicts or defeated royalists entering the colony, but to determine the relative influence the various social classes had upon the society in which they lived. Although the number of "cavaliers" fleeing Cromwell's success in England may have been small, the attitude of wellborn Virginians—those who maintained their loyalty to the Stuart kings whether, like Berkeley, they arrived in the colony before the English Civil Wars or after—did pervade and influence that society. To say that Virginia was, in portions of the seventeenth century, a cavalier society, does not mean that it was composed primarily of exiled royalists, but merely that the society, through its leaders, breathed loyalty to Charles I and II as its guiding principle. This principle, as has been pointed out, was eroded in the latter part of the seventeenth century, and it not unnaturally lost some of its meaning when the Stuarts lost their throne and their power in England and when the number of English-born Virginia colonists declined. The influence of an English birth, an English education, and an English upbringing on the Virginians of the seventeenth century cannot be underestimated. To English-born Virginians, England was "home." The "Americans" were the Indians. By the end of the seventeenth century time had erased this cultural heritage, despite the attempts of Virginians to educate their sons in England and despite frequent trips to their ancestral homeland. By the end of the seventeenth century Virginia was "home," the social restrictions on the acquisition of land or the exploitation of labor had been removed, and neither God nor king could exert the compulsive power, in contrast to the tug of growing individual prosperity and power, that they brought to bear in the early years of settlement.

One further point needs to be stressed. Why do we not find the likes of Sir William Berkeley, Captain John Smith, to say nothing of Thomas Jefferson, in Virginia today? The answer, I think, lies in the fact that Virginia in the colonial period was largely a self-contained power, with all the problems that face a powerful independent nation today. Vital decisions had to be made about dealing with what were essentially foreign powers, the Indians. Vital decisions about encouraging or discouraging tobacco growing and other economic measures had to be made within the

[28] *Op. cit.*, p. 32.

colony. The need to make such important decisions called forth the greatest talent and the highest powers of the individuals responsible. Governor William Bradford, leading a tiny colony of 100 settlers in Plymouth, was making the same types of decisions that a President of the United States is called upon to make today. So were John Smith and William Berkeley. Today foreign policy is in the hands of Washington officials, as are many aspects of state economic policy. Debate proceeds on the extent to which state power has been or ought to be turned over to the central government, but the facts of twentieth-century life are that no state can operate as an independent unit, or even as it operated as a colonial dependency of Great Britain. The demands for the highest talents are no longer made on a state level. It is for this reason, I suspect, that much talent is drawn physically out of the state to the central source of power, or to other fields of endeavor in the arts and sciences, or into the economic sphere.

What, then, can the seventeenth century teach us in the twentieth century? It can show us how a society operated before the full rush of the age of possessive individualism came upon us. Unmistakable signs today point toward a softening of the sharp edges of an individualistic society, not the least significant of which is the gradual exhaustion of a cheaply available land base. Our cities and countryside seem to require some guiding principle for individual actions other than individual gain if the society is to develop viably and validly. Individual corporations have recognized the need for a social conscience, and their plans take on a character that increasingly resembles the status society which we left behind. The worn-out workman, for example, has a place both within the market economy during his productive years and in the society as a whole during his nonproductive ones. Cities which, in an earlier era, could expand without community planning for transit lines, or reservation of park space, are now seen to require social, as well as individual, planning.

The seventeenth century, then, can reveal how a society which was more than the sum of its individual parts could operate. The royal symbol of its coherence as a society may no longer be applicable, but its essence may be recaptured in some other symbol. The flag serves as that symbol for the soldier who reveres something beyond himself, and other segments of society—nurses, professors—seek goals beyond their individual well-being. When all elements of society coalesce in a mutually held reverence for something beyond self, then there is created a society with a purpose—a society greater than the sum of its parts. Virginia has experienced such a higher purpose several times in its history and may do so again, particularly if she remembers that her history is one of her richest assets and surest guides.

2

upon the colony as the basis of its economic system. The traffic in human freight, wrenched from tribal moorings in Africa, annually brought some 2,000 slaves into Virginia throughout the first three-quarters of the century. In consequence, by 1790 nearly one-half of the population was not only colored but in bondage for life.[3]

The white population during the first part of the eighteenth century was almost as completely English in composition as it had been during the preceding century. Whereas New England was to a large degree East Anglia transplanted to America, Virginia, or the region east of the Blue Ridge, was a cross section of all England disassembled and reunited in a different pattern. Life upon the plantation, however, shaped the character of the Virginia planter and differentiated him from the English yeoman or squire. He became, in short, more and more a Virginian, less and less an Englishman.[4]

A thousand or so French Huguenots who came to the colony around 1700 were quickly assimilated by the dominant culture. But toward the middle of the century three different nationalities met in the Great Valley and set up their own ways of life. The northern section was claimed by Anglo-Virginians from the eastern sector of the state. The middle region was settled mainly by Germans from Pennsylvania. And the remoter middle and southern sections were settled by Scotch-Irish, who also arrived by way of the northern province. Despite a tendency of the frontier to weld diverse elements thus thrown together, the Germans and Scots for generations clung to their distinctive ways of life.[5]

The Germans, unaccustomed to elementary self-government in their native homes, brought little political ambition in their cultural luggage. The Scotch-Irish, on the other hand, were self-reliant and fiercely independent, qualities that made them resent any interference in their affairs by the Tidewater planters. The Valley was to remain a region chiefly of white men, yeomen let us say, raising livestock and cultivating cereals. Travelers later testified that agriculture was conducted better there than east of the Blue Ridge.[6]

Society in Virginia during the eighteenth century, save in the Valley, was stratified and had its hierarchy of ranks. Cheap land and a severe

[3] Gilliam, *op. cit.*, pp. 11, 106; Thomas J. Wertenbaker, *The Old South* (New York, 1942), p. 5; Abbot E. Smith, *Colonists in Bondage* (Chapel Hill, N.C., 1947), pp. 29–30, 335–37; Lewis C. Gray, *History of Agriculture in the Southern United States* (New York, 1961), I, 349–56, 361–64; William E. Hemphill, *Cavalier Commonwealth* (New York, 1957), p. 119.

[4] Bridenbaugh, *Myths and Realities*, p. 3; Wertenbaker, *op. cit.*, pp. 3, 6.

[5] Richard L. Morton, *Colonial Virginia* (Chapel Hill, N.C., 1960), I, 367–69, II, 444–46; Albert B. Faust, *The German Element in the United States* (New York, 1927), pp. 177–211; Wertenbaker, *op. cit.*, pp. 166–219.

[6] Klaus G. Wust, "German Immigrants and Nativism in Virginia," in Society for the History of Germans in Maryland, *Twenty-ninth Report* (Baltimore, 1956), p. 32; Jean Gottmann, *Virginia at Mid-Century* (New York, 1955), p. 96.

shortage of labor, however, provided economic opportunities that led to a somewhat open, mobile class structure, which in turn permitted easy advancement for men with ambition and ability.

At the base of the structure were the Negro slaves, who, despite their rock-bottom station, proved a potent force in the land. As the largest single element in the population, they held the Old Dominion on its singular course. "Every aspect of life," explains Carl Bridenbaugh, "bore the impress of the slave, from the introduction of Africanisms into the language to the crystallization of social needs and customs in provincial legal codes." In bondage for life, inarticulate, lacking leaders, property, status, and political power, the blacks were nevertheless a determining element in Virginia's cultural formula.[7]

Indentured servants comprised the lowest echelon of the white hierarchy. Somewhat over one-third of the white immigrants to the Chesapeake region prior to the Revolution arrived in bondage. Many of the newcomers after 1728 were Irish and some were German, but English immigration recommenced after 1768. Included in this segment of society were some 20,000 convicts transported to the Chesapeake region during the eighteenth century, at least one-third of whom were unloaded on Virginia.[8]

The lower class of whites, who had no land or at best an old worn-out field on which to raise a few pounds of tobacco or some wheat, were fewer in colonial Virginia than anywhere else in the world. Owning no slaves, uneducated, enjoying no political influence, they were despised even by the Negroes. They were noted for their avoidance of labor and their consumption of peach brandy and hard cider.[9]

Fortunately for the future of the province, a large percentage of its white inhabitants who were not in bondage or rejoicing in indolence comprised a class of lesser planters who, perhaps with the aid of a few slaves, cultivated their own tobacco fields. Despite their tendency to migrate, this yeomanlike element steadily increased, fed by the younger sons of richer planters and by successful recruits, such as plantation overseers, from the servant ranks. Many of its representatives proved ambitious and enterprising and won footholds in the ranks of the gentry.[10]

Presiding over the hierarchy was a ruling class comparable in its own

[7] Bridenbaugh, *Myths and Realities*, p. 6.

[8] Smith, *op. cit.*, pp. 119, 330–31, 337; Bridenbaugh, *Myths and Realities*, p. 7; Douglas S. Freeman, *George Washington* (New York, 1948), I, 84–87.

[9] Bridenbaugh, *Myths and Realities*, p. 8; Wertenbaker, *op. cit.*, pp. 11; Gray, *op. cit.*, I, 483–87.

[10] Gilliam, *op. cit.*, p. 14; Bridenbaugh, *Myths and Realities*, pp. 8–10; Harry R. Merrens, *Colonial North Carolina in the Eighteenth Century* (Chapel Hill, N.C., 1964), pp. 19–24; Gray, *op. cit.*, I, 488–92; R. E. and B. K. Brown, *Virginia, 1705–1786* (East Lansing, Mich., 1964), pp. 46–54.

setting to a European aristocracy. Wealth, lavishly displayed in landed estates, sumptuous mansions, and scores of slaves, provided admission to this patrician order, which looked to England not only for political and economic direction, but also for the patterns in which it should shape its everyday life. The earliest fortunes were founded on tobacco, but wheat growing, the production of naval stores and iron, lumbering, shipbuilding, and even trade supplemented in time the activities of the great planters. The acquisition of new lands was an easy road to affluence, and another avenue leading to the top was through a successful marriage. No scruples, Bridenbaugh concludes, deterred the colonial fortune hunter, not even great differences in ages. A twenty-three-year-old Henrico County youth, for example, married a widow of eighty-five, described as "a sprightly old Tit, with Three Thousand pounds fortune."[11]

A land policy favoring the few was second only to the slave system in creating an aristocractic society. Land, not the culture of tobacco or mercantile ventures, made the descendants of Robert "King" Carter, one of early eighteenth-century Virginia's largest landholders, a power in Virginia for generations to come. Sheer extravagance obscured the fact that virtually all of the planters were deeply in debt to English and Scottish merchants, that the agrarian economy of the colony was decaying as early as 1750 with little prospects for recovery. Yet, even though the aristocracy was based on an unsound economy and now and then on actual fraud, there was "much in it that was admirable as it reached its fullest development at the time of the Revolution."[12]

The attachment of the established families to the social order and government giving them prominence and seeming prosperity was enduring. Good fortune in family environment, traditions, and relationships; superior educational advantages extending possibly to Oxford or Cambridge; familiarity with the idealism of the Enlightenment; responsibilities of plantation and parish management; and the thought-provoking experience of living in a revolutionary era were among the circumstances that made Edmund Pendleton, George Mason, Jefferson, Washington, Madison, and their colleagues fit for high responsibilities. The singular role played by Virginia in the founding of the new republic and its influence on national affairs well into the next century, however, were due to a small number of Virginians rather than to the collective attitudes or endeavors of the whole population.[13]

Neither the needs nor the efforts of a sparsely settled province

[11] Bridenbaugh, *Myths and Realities,* pp. 10–14.
[12] Wertenbaker, *op. cit.,* p. 346; Emory G. Evans, "Planter Indebtedness and the Coming of the Revolution in Virginia," *William and Mary Quarterly,* 3d ser., XIX (1962), 517–25; Freeman, *op. cit.,* I, 169.
[13] Charles S. Sydnor, *Gentlemen Freeholders* (Chapel Hill, N.C., 1952), pp. 1–10; Gottmann, *op. cit.,* p. 89.

produced an extensive system of schools. The scheme which evolved closely paralleled that in England: apprentice education for a laboring class confined to agriculture; tutorial education for the scions of the rich planters; a few endowed Latin grammar schools for those aspiring to the professions; and the College of William and Mary for training clergymen and destined leaders of the Commonwealth. On the whole, education was to remain a luxury in the Old Dominion until after the Civil War.[14]

Virginia's rate of population increase during the eighteenth century averaged 27.5 percent each decade, while that of the entire country was 34.5 percent. The growth rates of New York, Maryland, North Carolina, and Georgia were equal to or greater than those of the Old Dominion in practically every decade. But Virginia's age and rapid early growth offset its gradual decrease so that in 1790 it was the most populous state in the new republic.[15]

Life in the Old Dominion at the end of the century, with a social structure barely ruffled by the Revolution, was still dominated by a rural environment. Definite improvements in health had been promoted by rising standards of living and the development of a colonial-born population. Although the growth of cities and towns was dependent upon reliable transportation facilities, the sheer abundance of navigable waterways in eastern Virginia, enabling the plantations to have private wharves giving access to the world, had initially militated against urbanization. Indeed, less than 2 percent of the population in 1790 lived in urban centers. Without such focal points, the colony did not even produce the tiny hamlets that dotted the northern provinces. The extension of population beyond the fall line and the creation of a rudimentary system of roads finally permitted the growth of such settlements as Alexandria, Richmond, and Petersburg.[16]

Related to this was a failure to give birth and support to a middle class of artisans and tradesmen. The use of Negro craftsmen on the plantations tended, by lowering wages and casting a stigma on skilled labor, to run white men out of the trades. The absence of white artisans was acutely felt, for they would have provided a sorely needed element of strength and democracy in a society economically unsound and basically aristocratic.[17]

In 1800 Virginia, still the most populous state, was represented in the

[14] Cornelius J. Heatwole, *A History of Education in Virginia* (New York, 1916), p. x; Freeman, *op. cit.*, I, 128–34; J. L. B. Buck, *The Development of Public Schools in Virginia* (Richmond, 1952), pp. 1–24. [15] Gilliam, *op. cit.*, pp. 15, 82.
[16] *Ibid.*, 85; John Duffy, *Epidemics in Colonial America* (Baton Rouge, La., 1953), pp. 242–47.
[17] Carl Bridenbaugh, *The Colonial Craftsman* (New York, 1950), pp. 1–32; Wertenbaker, *op. cit.*, pp. 232, 269–70; Freeman, *op. cit.*, I, 145–47.

lower house of Congress by twenty-two members, and in 1810 gained another. But its glitter was fading. The Negroes, increasing extravagantly because of the peculiar farming practices of the region, in turn served to perpetuate those pursuits: their white masters were simply unable to devise any occupations for them save field assignments. Their presence, moreover, hampered the growth of industry, for it seemed impossible to develop the area's natural resources on the basis of slave labor, and neither free labor nor capital was willing to venture into a slave state.[18]

The importation of slaves was finally forbidden by the legislature in 1806, and two years later Congress extended the prohibition to the entire country. Domestic slave trading thereupon became a new and profitable activity when, after 1815, the cotton plantations of the deep South began to expand and require abundant labor. Virginia led in the sale of blacks to the new regions, becoming a nursery for commercial slave breeding. By 1830 the proportion of Negroes in the total population reached 48 percent, an all-time high. The traffic in slaves between 1830 and 1840, to cite one decade, accounted for the annual expatriation of 12,000 Negroes. This depletion offset their high rate of natural increase, so that from 1840 until the Civil War the colored population grew less than half as fast as the white. Yet the number of free colored persons in Virginia increased from 20,000 in 1800 to 55,000 in 1860, in stark contrast to Mississippi, where the number between 1840 and 1860 declined 50 percent.[19]

The peopling of the western reaches of Virginia, mainly by whites with strong democratic attitudes, had in the meanwhile proceeded briskly. Indeed, as early as 1800 over 200,000 Virginians were living beyond the Blue Ridge. Their spokesmen argued in 1816 that the state's constitution should be revised because more whites were residing west of the Blue Ridge than east of it, yet the representation system obtaining in the legislature was assuring a large majority to the slaveholding Piedmont and Tidewater.[20]

Tobacco cultivation, like the white population, also moved westward after 1800. Following the discovery that lands exhausted through repetitious planting of tobacco would produce wheat and corn, a gradual shift to the cultivation of grains got under way. The introduction of the iron plow and other farm machinery, plus the use of fertilizers, eventually led to a resurgence in agriculture, ironically enough, in the decade proceding

[18] John R. Alden, *The First South* (Baton Rouge, La., 1961), p. 15; Gray, *op. cit.*, I, 444–45, II, 760–69; *Biographical Directory of the American Congress, 1774–1961* (Washington, D.C., 1961), p. 45.
[19] Ulrich B. Phillips, *American Negro Slavery* (New York, 1929), pp. 132–49; Gray, *op. cit.*, II, 658–69; Gilliam, *op. cit.*, pp. 37, 106; Francis B. Simkins, *The South Old and New* (New York, 1947), p. 61.     [20] Gottmann, *op. cit.*, pp. 99–100.

the Civil War. Tobacco, however, continued to dominate the Old Dominion's economy.[21]

In no decade between 1800 and 1860 did Virginia sustain a population increase of more than 13 percent. It ceased being the most populous state in 1820 and by 1860 had dropped to fifth place. Its congressional delegation accordingly fell from 23 representatives in 1810 to 11 in 1860. From 1830 to 1840, when the flow of outbound slaves and migrating whites became a flood, its population actually declined 2 percent. And although its total population increased 50 percent between 1800 and 1860, that of New York, in contrast, increased 600 percent, Massachusetts 300 percent, Pennsylvania 500 percent, and North Carolina 200 percent. Virginia's slow rate of growth was caused not only by the migration of its people to areas promising greater opportunities, but also by its failure to attract white immigrants.[22]

A sagging economy, a society still offering few chances for the poor man to improve his condition in life, and insufficient industrial activity to lure immigrants from foreign countries discouraged white immigration throughout the antebellum period. In 1850, 91 percent of the white and free colored inhabitants were natives, 6.5 percent were born in other states, and 2.5 percent were foreign-born. In the same year such states as Massachusetts showed a 16 percent foreign-born population, New York 21 percent, and Pennsylvania 13 percent. The only states out of the original thirteen with fewer foreign-born inhabitants in 1850 than Virginia were those farther south.[23]

Virginia, on the other hand, had long been serving as a "feeder" of human resources to other regions. The process was enormously accelerated during the first half of the nineteenth century. Although figures covering the full phenomenon are wanting, the 1850 census found 55,000 white and free colored natives of Virginia residing in Kentucky, 47,000 in Tennessee, 86,000 in Ohio, 42,000 in Indiana, 25,000 in Illinois, and 41,000 in Missouri. In all, 388,000 white and free colored persons claiming the Old Dominion as their place of birth were, in 1850, living outside the state, which at that time had 949,000 white and free colored inhabitants. No other state suffered such a depletion of its human resources.[24]

A study devoted to Virginia's exportation of political talent has shown that 232 congressmen representing other states were born in the Old Dominion prior to 1810. Massachusetts, in contrast, sent 147 future

[21] Gray, *op. cit.*, II, 754–857; Joseph C. Robert, *The Tobacco Kingdom* (Durham, N.C., 1938), pp. 15–17; Gottman, *op. cit.*, pp. 101–4.

[22] Gilliam, *op. cit.*, pp. 14–15, 83–84; *Biog. Directory of Amer. Congress*, p. 45; U.S. Census, 12th, *Population* (Washington, D.C., 1901), I, xxii–xxiii.

[23] J. D. B. De Bow, *Statistical View of the United States* (Washington, D.C., 1854), pp. 116–18.    [24] *Ibid.*

congressmen born before 1810 to other states, and South Carolina, potentially a feeder to the same areas as Virginia, supplied only 23. The Virginia expatriate born before 1810 who climbed highest was William Henry Harrison, but among others were 15 United States cabinet officers and 9 state and 12 territorial governors. Inasmuch as the traditionally poor white family pushing west or southwest rarely supplied political leaders in the new regions, it is obvious that Virginia, through migration, lost a goodly percentage of its favored as well as well as hundreds of thousands of its less-privileged sons and daughters.[25]

Antebellum improvements in transportation facilities provided, again ironically on the eve of the Civil War, a stimulus to the state's economic life. The railroad expansion era of the 1840's and 1850's, rendering virtually obsolete a traditional dependence upon waterways, created powerful regional links and reoriented the territorial divisions of the Commonwealth. These internal improvements were largely responsible for the presence in Virginia in 1850 of some 12,000 persons claiming Ireland as their place of birth. They were accessories to the fact that the Old Dominion in 1861 had 1,800 miles of railways in operation, 22 percent more than any other Southern state and 18 percent of the nation's total.[26]

Related to improved transportation facilities was the growth of cities and towns. Although the urban population, however, increased 942 percent between 1790 and 1860, it still comprised somewhat less than 10 percent of the state's total population in the latter year. During the same interval the urban populations of New York increased 3,887 percent, Pennsylvania 2,029 percent, and Maryland 1,727 percent. By 1860 the world had passed through the first stages of the industrial revolution and trade liberalization, and the United States was actively participating in the expansion of urban activities and the gathering of wealth. New York City showed in 1860 a population of 805,000, Philadelphia 562,000, and Baltimore 212,000; Richmond, Virginia's largest city, had a population of only 38,000 inhabitants.[27]

Yet in Richmond was concentrated the essence of urban civilization in Virginia. A trickle of French *émigrés* during the 1790's had added to the tone of a Scottish mercantile outpost, the horizons of which were broadened in the 1840's and 1850's by an influx of newly arrived Germans. The 1850 census uncovered some 5,000 natives of Germany resident in the state, constituting next to the Irish the only appreciable

[25] Richard B. Davis, "The Jeffersonian Expatriate in the Building of the Nation," *Virginia Magazine of History and Biography*, LXX (1962), 49–61.

[26] Gottmann, *op. cit.*, pp. 104–9; U.S. Census, 8th, *Preliminary Report* (Washington, D.C., 1862), pp. 234–35; De Bow, *op. cit.*, pp. 116–18.

[27] Gottmann, *op. cit.*, pp. 127–28; Gilliam, *op. cit.*, pp. 85–88; U.S. Census, 8th, *op. cit.*, pp. 242–44.

foreign-born element in the Old Dominion. In 1861 Germans accounted for 25 percent of the white population of Richmond. But even then the capital city displayed in its best sections the same elegant mode of life led by the planter aristocracy. A large part of its working population consisted of slaves, wageless, subsisting upon the cheapest food, and constituting insurmountable competition to free labor.[28]

The isolation of the plantations and the absence of urban centers had given Virginia an advantage in the matter of health during the preceding century. The development of cities and towns and the improvement of transportation facilities during the nineteenth century, however, were accompanied by sundry epidemics—yellow fever, Asiatic cholera, typhoid fever, smallpox, and others—that from time to time disrupted the normal activities of Norfolk, Portsmouth, Richmond, and Alexandria. Although on the whole epidemics affected the blacks much the same as the whites, the former seemed particularly susceptible to respiratory diseases, yet generally possessed more immunity than whites to smallpox, yellow fever, and malaria.[29]

Uncovered by the 1840 census were 59,000 illiterates in Virginia's white population of 740,000 persons, a shocking ratio of 1 to 12.5. The same census established ratios of 1 to 164 in Massachusetts, 1 to 300 in New Hampshire, and 1 to 49 in Pennsylvania. Massachusetts, with less white population than Virginia, had 160,000 pupils attending primary schools in 1840, of whom 158,000 were studying at public charge. Virginia, on the other hand, had only 35,000 pupils in primary schools, fewer than 10,000 of whom were on public charge. Public education, in short, had found no place in the social fabric of the Old Dominion, despite Thomas Jefferson's enlightened efforts on its behalf.[30]

The ruling patricians were more interested in higher and secondary education than in a system of primary schools. The 1850 census, as a matter of fact, showed that Virginia had more young men in her higher institutions of learning in proportion to her white population than Massachusetts, New York, or Pennsylvania. But, alas, the same census showed also that the percentage of native whites in school in Virginia was 12.3, the lowest in the country with the exception of frontier Florida and California. The percentage of illiterates in the total white population in 1850 stood at 8.6; only five states, all farther south, had higher rates.[31]

Virginia, probably more than any other Southern state, felt the awful impact of the Civil War. A large part of its territory and 25 percent of its

[28] De Bow, *op. cit.*, p. 117; Wust, *op. cit.*, pp. 33–38.
[29] Wyndham B. Blanton, *Medicine in Virginia in the Nineteenth Century* (Richmond, 1933), pp. 224–71; Duffy, *op. cit.*, pp. 244–46.
[30] Gottmann, *op. cit.*, pp. 115–17; Buck, *op. cit.*, pp. 25–64.
[31] Heatwole, *op. cit.*, pp. 137–209; De Bow, *op. cit.*, p. 150.

white population were lost through the secession of West Virginia; the physical destruction of property was devastating; and the disorganization of the economic system was almost complete. The sudden liberation of half a million slaves, hopelessly unprepared to enjoy freedom, destroyed not only a labor system but also a political and social order. It was an impoverished and prostrate commonwealth that attained readmission to the Union in 1870. Yet, as horrible as it was, the Civil War in essence had extricated Virginia's people from the blind alley which they entered in the eighteenth century.

After 1870 the population of the state increased at an average rate of 11 percent each decade, while that of the entire country increased at a rate of 24.7 percent. Virginia's white population, however, achieved a degree of stability and increased at an average rate of 16 percent each decade, whereas the colored population averaged a 9.4 percent increase each decade from 1860 to 1880 and dropped to less than 1 percent between 1880 and 1890. As a result, the proportion of whites in the total population rose from 56.7 percent in 1860 to 64.3 percent in 1900.[32]

Yet each postbellum decade found more native Virginians living in other states than persons born in other states or foreign countries residing in Virginia. Over 28 percent of the total number of persons born in Virginia—a staggering 683,000 expatriates—were living elsewhere in the United States in 1880. And the cumulative net loss of whites through-out the latter decades of the century was greater than that of Negroes. It was too poor a land and saddled with too many problems to attract many of the new immigrants arriving in the country. It strove officially and through private channels to be alluring, but failed.[33]

The collapse of the plantation system, combined with a general agricultural depression after the Civil War, caused many landowners to abandon the management of their estates and take up businesses and professions in cities and towns. They were joined in the trek by a great mass of rural Negroes who were unable to acquire land of their own and who discovered that tenant farming was little better than slavery. The large estates, one by one, were broken up into smaller units, so that the average size of Virginia's farms fell from 336 acres in 1860 to 119 acres in 1900.[34]

It was, to be sure, a period of painful reorganization for the state's agricultural economy. And, alas, farm products were cheap, for a great agricultural expansion was concurrently taking place both within the United States and abroad. Virginia's small farms could hardly compete

---

[32] Gilliam, *op. cit.*, pp. 37, 82, 106.
[33] U.S. Census, 10th, *Population* (Washington, D.C., 1883), p. 483; Gilliam, *op. cit.*, pp. 52–53; William H. Gaines, "New Blood for the Old Dominion," *Virginia Cavalcade*, II (Summer 1952), 39–43.      [34] Hemphill, *op. cit.*, p. 358.

in production with the wide open spaces being put to work in the Middle West. Yet, in the final decades of the century, counties along the Carolina border found an answer to the competition of Kentucky's cheap burley tobacco by turning to bright leaf; the Eastern Shore was transformed into a vegetable garden; peanuts and hams became profitable products of the Norfolk-Petersburg area; fruit growers extended their orchards along both slopes of the Blue Ridge; and livestock husbandry became a thriving specialty of the Valley and Southwest Plateau.[35]

The transportation network, shattered by the Civil War, passed into the hands of Northern capitalists and was rebuilt before the end of the century, stimulating not only agricultural progress but also commercial and industrial developments. While Virginia's share of the tobacco industry as a whole declined, the growing popularity of cigarettes—and Lewis Ginter's wit in perceiving the trend—turned Richmond into the cigarette capital of the world. Lumbering expanded to the point where Virginia in 1900 ranked fifteenth among the states as a producer and enjoyed a variety of related manufacturing activities. Mineral resources, including iron and the coal deposits of the southwest, were put to work, leading to machine manufacturing in such centers as Richmond and Roanoke.[36]

A somewhat cosmopolitan constitutional convention, composed of "scalawags, Negroes, and carpet-baggers," in 1869 adopted provisions for a system of public education which were subsequently guaranteed by the act of Congress readmitting Virginia to the Union. But implementation of the program was handicapped by the fact that the state treasury, because of an inability to meet the staggering interest accumulations on antebellum internal improvement bonds, was deeply in debt. Payment of the public debt, in the eyes of a conservative leadership returned to power in the 1870's, was more important than maintaining the new free school system. It was obvious, though, that something had to be done about the education of the Negroes as well as the mounting number of whites impoverished by the Civil War. The white illiterates in the state, for example, increased 30 percent between 1860 and 1870.[37]

Despite fiscal, political, and social obstacles, a public school system was inaugurated with enrollments increasing from 131,000 pupils in 1871 to 370,000 in 1900. It was none too soon as the 1880 census recorded that 41 percent of the total population was unable to read and write. This awesome statistic included 18.5 percent of the whites. The new system of schools began to pay off when the 1890 census reported a 25 percent reduction in illiteracy. But the twentieth century opened with

[35] Gottmann, *op. cit.*, pp. 124–25.
[36] U.S. Census, 12th, *Manufactures* (Washington, D.C., 1902), II, 906–9.
[37] Heatwole, *op. cit.*, pp. 213–35; Buck, *op. cit.*, pp. 65–93.

23 percent of the total population—11 percent of the whites and 45 percent of the Negroes—classified as illiterate.[38]

Virginia crossed the threshold of the present century with 1,854,000 inhabitants, only 1 percent of whom were foreign-born. In fact, 92 percent of its people were natives of the state, scions of English, Scottish, Irish, German, and African tribal stock, with here and there a surname denoting origins in France. The proportion of Negroes in the total population, now reduced to 35 percent, was following a steady downward trend, forecasting an even greater decline in the coming decades as their northward movement gained momentum. Just as the Old Dominion had turned to public education in its belated assault on illiteracy, so also by 1900 were steps being taken, through a Board of Health organized in 1872, to improve sanitary conditions and the health of the citizenry in general. Indeed, sentiment was actually forming in favor of more state activity in promoting social welfare.[39]

The Civil War, Francis B. Simkins maintains, had freed the common white man as surely as it had liberated the Negro by eliminating the competition of slave labor and permitting the importation of Northern ideas of the dignity of labor that reconciled the whites to many forms of work from which they had formerly been excluded by social prejudices. Virginia's gainfully employed labor force on the threshold of the twentieth century embraced 48 percent of its total population aged ten and over. A steady decline in the proportion of agricultural workers after 1880 was offset by increased employment in industry, trade, and transportation. While 45 percent of all persons at work in 1900 were still on the farm, 11 percent were engaged in trade and transportation, and 17 percent in manufacturing and mechanical pursuits.[40]

As agriculture languished and the decline of the planter class crippled its appeal as an avenue to wealth and social distinction, men of industry and commerce assumed economic and political control. But the debacle at Appomattox had generated nostalgic sentiment for the social ideals of an Old Dominion that flowered in the eighteenth century. And although men of industry and commerce by 1900 constituted a new governing class, they were often moved by traditions derived from an agrarian society and themselves assumed the trappings of the planter aristocracy.

Compared with the growth of the great Northern cities, that of Virginia's urban centers by 1900 was not impressive, yet was full of significance for the future. The urban concentration of population

[38] Heatwole, *op. cit.*, pp. 240–45; U.S. Census, 10th, *op. cit.*, pp. 919–25; U.S. Census, 12th, *Population,* II, c.      [39] U.S. Census, 12th, *Population,* I, ciii, cxiv.
[40] Simkins, *op. cit.*, p. 213; U.S. Census, 12th, *Occupations* (Washington, D.C., 1904), pp. 154–65.

between 1860 and 1900 increased 300 percent, while that of the rural areas increased only 27 percent. Although many of the people who moved from country to city and from farm to factory retained their rural ideals, it was nevertheless obvious by 1900 that the Old Dominion was on the verge of discovering the amenities and economic advantages of urbanization.[41]

As recently as 1935 a native of Alabama piously voiced the following hopes in a book published in North Carolina:

In a sense it is a sacrilege to speak of commercial progress in connection with Virginia. One might wish that the community-development bodies could hold their peace in that state. Virginia really should be endowed. Nobody should have to make a living there. In a state so perfectly designed to serve as a background for mellowed charm and quiet grace, where long ago the brash surgings of the pioneers were softened under the influence of a mature civilization, it is fitting that there should be a solicitude only for harmony among men, and for sweetness and light.[42]

He was thirty-five years too late. The people of Virginia, in a moment of truth, were re-entering the main stream of national life at the turn of the century.

[41] Gilliam, *op. cit.*, p. 85.
[42] Clarence E. Cason, "Middle Class and Bourbon," in *Culture in the South*, ed. W. T. Couch (Chapel Hill, N.C., 1935), p. 491.

3

# The Changing Density of Virginia's Population: Urbanization and Migration

*Rupert B. Vance*

*The University of North Carolina*

It may aid in our analysis of Virginia's changing pattern of people on the land to suggest that this country was presettled, settled, and is now being resettled. The United States was presettled by a process of dispersion in which pioneers appropriated vacant lands—vacant, that is, except for hostile Indians, who could hardly be expected to approve of the proceedings. It then achieved agricultural settlement by farmers who filled the land up to a certain maximum density attainable by a handicraft agriculture. In the main, the first two essays have dealt with Virginia's part in these proceedings.

The first stage—presettlement—was ended for the United States when the Census Bureau in 1880 announced the disappearance of the frontier as represented by a density of six or fewer persons per square mile. Agricultural settlement was led by the covered wagon and the homesteader. It appears to have reached its maximum just before mechanization and scientific practices in agriculture began to push farmers off the land.

Essays 1 and 2 indicate that Virginia as our first settled colony is not too clearly represented by this summary treatment of what was essentially the westward movement. The country has long been in the process of resettlement by convergence and concentration in large cities and metropolitan areas. Virginia is caught up in this third movement—one that can best be viewed in terms of the state's participation in major national and regional trends.


*Urbanization and the Density of Settlement*

The distribution of people over the land—the pattern of settlement—has a useful index number, that of population density. Like the size of the community, this appears to be a function of urbanization, which in turn can be regarded as a function of the complexity of the economy—its economic distance from the frontier, if you please. It is also seen as a function of the extent to which population is retained in rural areas; this is a process which may be uneconomic, as witness portions of the Southern Appalachians.

The extreme range of population distribution in space—from high concentration at one end to sparsity of settlement at the other—in this country is surprising when one begins to study it. In 1960 our urban population amounted to almost 70 percent of the country's total. It was concentrated in slightly more than 1 percent of the United States' land area.

Obviously in America we huddle close together. The degree to which we huddle together decreases as the size of the community decreases—a thing to be expected. For cities of a million or more, population density in 1960 was 13,865 persons per square mile; between communities of a hundred thousand and a million population it was from 4,000 to 6,000 persons per square mile; in places of 2,500 to 5,000, the lowest range of urban communities, it was 1,446. In the urban fringes of settlement, areas just outside the city's legal limits, it averaged 1,781 persons per square mile; but in the rural territory of the United States we now have an average settlement of only 15 people per square mile.

In its simplest aspects urbanization is seen as a concentration of people in restricted localities followed by the multiplication, the expansion, and the fusion of these concentrations. So far, this process has shown no signs of abating. The farm population now represents only 7.7 percent of the nation's total, and the nation is still trying to cut back surplus agricultural production. Many people who own or cultivate farms today do not live on them; contrarywise many who live on them do not work there or on any other farm. Specialists in the United States Census Bureau long ago told us that the residential and occupational categories in the farm population are not to be confused. This caution must be held in mind continually.

So far we are not able to predict a ceiling to the growth of metropolitan areas in the United States. We tend to see their growth as a function of the complexity of the economy as it moves from an extractive to an industrial stance with highly technical and professional services. Without efficient production in the agricultural sector and without that technology on the urban side which enables people to work and live in large concentrations—technology that enables us to purify and store water, dispose of wastes, and transport and preserve food—our great concentrations would not prove feasible. It is remarkable that Rome and other cities of antiquity partially solved many of these problems.

Our country began its census count with an average of 4.5 people per square mile; it counted 50.5 in 1960. From 1910 to 1960, a half-century period, the population density of the coterminous United States increased from 31 to 60 persons per square mile. In Virginia it increased from 51 to approximately 100 persons per square mile.

In regard to urbanism, Virginia resembles a man who, after spending his boyhood in rustic haunts, in his maturity becomes enamored of city life. In 1900 the state had only 27 urban places; in 1960 there were 76. In 1900 Virginia had 300,241 people living in places of 5,000 inhabitants or more; in 1960 there were 1,730,576 inhabitants in cities of 5,000 and more, and 1,249,847 lived in places of 50,000 and over. Only 4.1 percent of the state's population live in hamlets of under 1,000 up to 2,500, but 40.2 percent live in other rural territory.

At the first United States census, taken in 1790, Virginia had four settlements of urban status: Alexandria, 2,748; Petersburg, 2,828; Norfolk, 2,959; and Richmond, 3,761. In contrast, North Carolina as late as 1840 contained no population center worthy to be called urban. Arkansas, Mississippi, Tennessee, and Florida territory kept it company. Other Virginia cities reached urban dimensions—2,500 population—rather late: Fredericksburg, 3,308, and Lynchburg, 4,630, in 1830; Portsmouth, 6,477, and Winchester, 3,454, in 1840. Roanoke jumped from 699 population in 1860 to 16,150 in 1870. In 1870 Charlottesville first attained urban status with 2,838, as did Danville with 3,463. Waynesboro, a hamlet of 856 in 1900, did not become urban until 1930 with 6,226. Martinsville also entered urban circles with 3,368 people in 1930. Williamsburg, Virginia's colonial capital, had a population of 1,344 in 1790. It did not attain urban status until the 1910 census, with 2,714. Restoration and all, the city had not climbed above 8,000 in 1960.

In 1960 Virginia, 55.8 percent urban, had 76 places of 2,500 population and over; in its rural areas it had 187 places from 1,000 to 2,500 population. On the highly urban side, 9 of its cities were 50,000 and over; and the state had, of course, 6 metropolitan areas. Map I provides an overview of population concentration as it existed in 1960. For the record it can be said that since 1962 the state has had 34 independent cities and 96 counties. Some of these cities are rather small in population.

In the higher density of urbanization, Virginia's procedures—while they baffle the outsider with their independent cities—allow the student to develop the range of urban density easily. It runs from 5,013 in the town of Norton to 304,869 for Norfolk.

Virginia's over-all density now exceeds that of any other Southeastern state and is approached only by North Carolina, which has a density of 92. Since Virginia is only 55.8 percent urban, as compared to 74 percent for Florida, 75 percent for Texas, and 67.7 for the whole West South-Central Division, it is evident that the state also has retained a fairly high density in its rural population. In this characteristic, however, it is exceeded by North Carolina, which supports a density of 92 with a population that is only 39.5 percent urban.

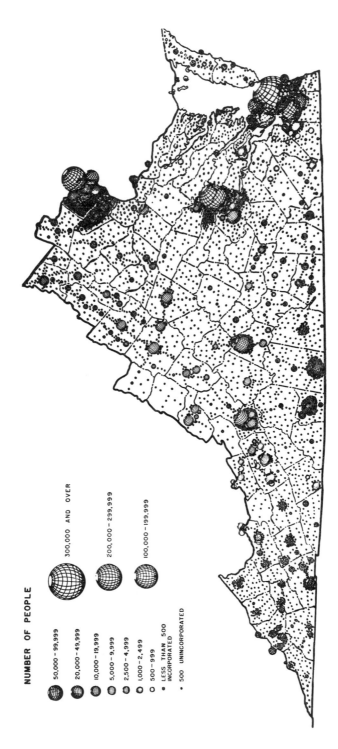

*1. Distribution of Virginia's people, 1960. (Courtesy of Agricultural Extension Service, Virginia Polytechnic Institute, Blacksburg, Virginia.)*

NUMBER OF PEOPLE

300,000 AND OVER

200,000 — 299,999

100,000 — 199,999

50,000 — 99,999

20,000 — 49,999

10,000 — 19,999

5,000 — 9,999

2,500 — 4,999

1,000 — 2,499

500 — 999

LESS THAN 500
INCORPORATED

500 UNINCORPORATED

Differences in county density of population are shown for the state in Map II. Variations in 1960 ranged from 7.7 persons per square mile in Highland, a mountain county largely uninhabited, to 6,808 in Arlington, a suburb of Washington. Map II indicates that Virginia in 1960 had 16 counties rather sparsely populated with a density of less than 25, 44 counties with 25 to 49, 25 counties with 50 to 99, and 13 counties with over 100 persons per square mile.

As Table 1 shows, almost two-thirds of Virginia's counties fail to

TABLE 1. VIRGINIA'S PATTERN OF DENSITY BY COUNTIES, 1960

| Categories | Population per square mile | | | |
|---|---|---|---|---|
| | Under 25 | 25 to 49.9 | 50 to 99.9 | 100 and over |
| Number of counties | 16 | 44 | 25 | 13 |
| Total population | 119,010 | 618,852 | 590,091 | 2,638,996 |
| Average county population | 8,000 | 14,065 | 23,604 | 203,000 |
| Percent of state's population | 3.0 | 15.6 | 14.9 | 64.5 |

*Source:* Computed from U.S. Bureau of the Census, *U.S. Census of Population: 1960, Virginia,* vol. I.

attain half the average density of the state, 50 persons per square mile. Those counties with a density of less than 25 had only 3 percent of the state's population and averaged less than 8,000 people per county. The 13 counties with a density of 100 and over included the 10 counties in metropolitan areas and contained 64.5 percent of the state's people. Counties with 25 to 50 people per square mile had an average of slightly over 14,000 people and contained 15.6 percent of the total population. Counties with a density from 50 to 100 had an average of 23,604 population and contained 14.9 percent of Virginia's people (Table 1).

## Migration and Population Growth

In the main, the counties of low density will continue to lose population and those of higher density will grow and overflow into contiguous areas. With due allowance for unique events to come, it would seem that the trends which prevailed from 1940 to 1960 are setting the pattern for Virginia's future development.

Map III shows how Virginia's counties shared population gains and losses from 1940 to 1950. It allocates the state's gain of 641,000 population from 1940 to 1950, a 23.9 percent increase, among its

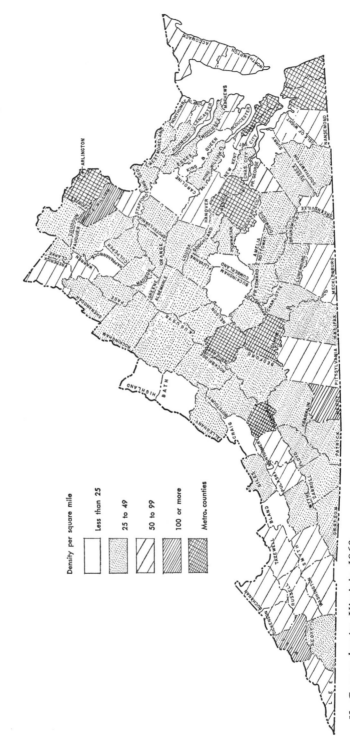

II. *County density, Virginia, 1960*

subregional areas. In the war period the natural increase of the state's population amounted to 67.5 percent, leaving a net inward migration of 208,157 to account for 32.5 percent of the gains.

More people moved from one place to another from 1940 to 1950 than in any other ten-year period in Virginia history.[1] The impact of World War II shifted population, and while some results were temporary, most of the migrations, it appears, advanced trends already established. The war decade confirmed the emergence of four new metropolitan areas. Although some 208,000 persons net moved in from other states, the tremendous shifting within the state seems to have been equally important. Workers moved into defense centers. The Hampton Roads area gained 153,000 persons from 1940 to 1944. In the decade from 1940 to 1950, 173,000 persons moved into this concentration. The continuation of the cold war meant that these centers retained a large share of the wartime gains. Virginia's overflow settlement from Washington, D.C., was to remain permanent, and the Richmond metropolitan area gained 13 percent by migration. Map IV shows very clearly the emergence of Virginia's "Urban Corridor." Continuing losses in rural counties with their unbalanced economies are evident in both Maps III and IV.

From 1950 to 1960 losses were concentrated in the Eastern Shore and the southwestern and south-central areas (Map IV). Is it not surprising to find that in spite of a population increase of 19.5 percent in the decade there were five subregions which had fewer people in 1960 than in 1950? They include the Eastern Shore, Central Piedmont, Central Southside, Central Southwest, and Cumberland subregions.

Along with these areas were a number of other subregions whose gains fell below those of natural increase, showing that they lost by migration. In addition to the five areas named above that lost population, the James-New River Highlands, the Blue Ridge Piedmont, the Roanoke-Radford Area, the Western Southside, the Midwest Piedmont, the Northwest Piedmont, the Upper Shenandoah, the Southern Tidewater, and the Northern Neck, as shown by Map V, all lost by net outward migration. Then follow certain areas whose migration gains were low. This includes the Lower Shenandoah, the Middle Peninsula, and the Richmond and Southside Hampton Roads areas, with net inward migrations of from 0.1 to 9 percent. The Roanoke-Radford area, which showed net inward migration in the 1940's, returned to outward migration in the 1950's.

Map V points up the importance of recent migrations. Virginia's population continued to grow with 1950 to 1960 showing an increase of 618,214 persons, or a percentage gain of 23.9. Of this, 95.4 percent,

---

[1] Sara K. Gilliam, in *University of Virginia News Letter*, Feb. 1, 1956.

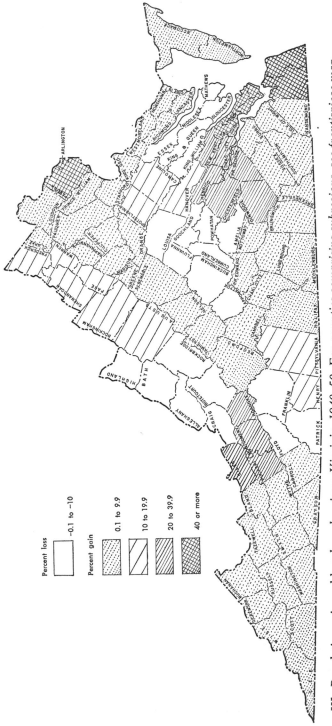

III. *Population gain and loss by subregions, Virginia, 1940–50. For counties comprising subregions, see frontispiece map.*

Lorin A. Thompson concluded, was due to natural increases—the excess of births over deaths within the state.[2] Just 4.6 percent was due to net inward migration. Nevertheless, urban areas continued their gains over rural territory as shown in Map V, a fact which indicates the large amount of economic readjustment which went on within the state. The "population scramble" continued the trend of people to huddle together, but those rural areas which failed to attract industry still sent their people elsewhere. Map V shows the extent to which migration gains were concentrated in the Urban Corridor: the Washington area and contiguous counties gained more than 20 percent by migration, with the Hampton Roads and York Peninsula areas in the next highest rate.

## Growth of Virginia's Metropolitan Areas

The American people are now moving into metropolitan areas, and Virginia as something of a statistical microcosm of the nation is following these trends. The movement to cities and out to the periphery is creating new patterns of life and work as expressed in changing densities of population. In the last census year the United States had 212 standard metropolitan statistical areas, containing about 62.7 percent of our total population. Virginia's six metropolitan areas did not fall far behind this national average; they contained 61 percent of the state's population.

Urban strips, it appears, grow by proximity, the fusion of contiguous areas. Thus we are hopefully told by chambers of commerce that Los Angeles will soon become a linear settlement extending for 200 miles up and down the Pacific Coast. A second conurbation is springing up, stretching from the New Jersey coast westward through Pittsburgh to Chicago with a trend toward the formation of one enormous more-or-less integrated urban strip.

On the East Coast people will not have to wait for this development. The one which most affects Virginia has already occurred. By 1960, 32 million people, one-sixth of the population of the coterminous United States, lived in 33 metropolitan areas, stretching from Boston to Washington, D.C., Maryland, and Virginia. Included are 43 separate cities and hundreds of ringing suburbs. Jean Gottmann has written of this as "Megalopolis, U.S.A." Map VI taken from his *Virginia at Mid-Century* shows how this impinges on northern Virginia.

Differing from the Southeast of which it is a part, Virginia thus appears to be the North of the South, or rather the entering wedge of the metropolitan North extending southward. Of the 2 million population in

[2] Lorin A. Thompson, "Virginia Population Change: Age and Color, 1950 and 1960," *ibid.*, June 15, 1961.

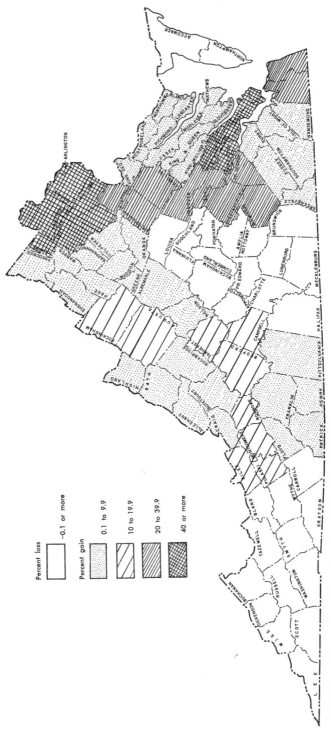

IV. *Population change by subregions, Virginia, 1950–60*

Percent loss

−0.1 or more

Percent gain

0.1 to 9.9

10 to 19.9

20 to 39.9

40 or more

the metropolitan area of Washington, 1,238,000 live outside the central city, in Maryland and Virginia. The central city lost 4.5 percent in population in the last decade while the outside areas gained 87 percent. Of this total, 539,618 live in Virginia (Table 2). Metropolitan Washington in Virginia consists of the counties of Arlington and Fairfax, with the cities of Alexandria and Falls Church and suburban areas extending farther into Loudoun and Prince William counties. All are in the corridor.

Table 2 serves to show the strength of metropolitan development in the

TABLE 2. THE POPULATION OF VIRGINIA AND ITS STANDARD METROPOLITAN STATISTICAL AREAS, 1960

| Metropolitan-nonmetropolitan residence | Total | Urban | | | Rural total |
|---|---|---|---|---|---|
| | | Total | Central city or cities | Other urban | |
| The state | 3,966,949 | 2,204,913 | 995,423 | 1,209,490 | 1,762,036 |
| In SMSA's: | 2,020,626 | 1,733,375 | 995,423 | 737,952 | 287,251 |
| In Virginia's Corridor | | | | | |
| 1. Washington, D.C., in Va. | 539,618 | 479,072 | | 479,072 | 60,546 |
| 2. Richmond, etc. | 408,494 | 336,436 | 219,958 | 116,478 | 72,058 |
| 3. Newport News—Hampton | 224,503 | 208,874 | 202,920 | 5,954 | 15,629 |
| 4. Norfolk—Portsmouth | 578,507 | 521,623 | 420,645 | 100,978 | 56,051 |
| Outside the "Corridor" | | | | | |
| 5. Lynchburg | 110,701 | 62,618 | 54,790 | 7,838 | 48,083 |
| 6. Roanoke | 158,803 | 124,752 | 97,110 | 27,642 | 34,051 |
| Not in standard metropolitan areas | 1,946,323 | 471,538 | | 471,538 | 1,474,785 |

*Source:* Computed from the Bureau of the Census, *Population: 1960, Virginia,* vol. I.

state. Over 2 million of the state's nearly 4 million people lived in six metropolitan areas of Virginia in 1960. Of Virginia's 2.2 million urban population, 1.7 million live here, leaving 471,538 urban dwellers scattered elsewhere throughout the state. But of the state's 1.8 million rural people only 287,251 are found in the metropolitan areas, leaving 1.5 million ruralites in the remaining part of the state. Further growth can be expected to spread outward from Virginia's metropolitan areas.

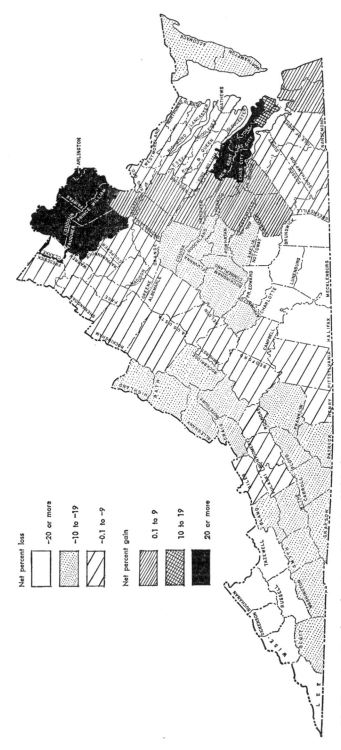

V. Net migration by subregions, Virginia, 1950–60

Net percent loss

-20 or more
-10 to -19
-0.1 to -9

Net percent gain

0.1 to 9
10 to 19
20 or more

It is here that we may begin to demarcate Virginia's urban strip—the Urban Corridor, well-named and analyzed by Lorin A. Thompson. Some twenty counties stretching from the banks of the Potomac through Petersburg, Hopewell, and Richmond to Northside and Southside Hampton Roads with Newport News, Norfolk, and Portsmouth contained 2,077,504 Virginia people in 1960 as compared to 1,889,445 for the rest of the state.[3] Of the 2 million in the corridor, only 18.5 percent lived outside its four metropolitan areas. The corridor has 1.7 million of the state's metropolitan population leaving 270,000 in the Roanoke and Lynchburg areas (Table 2). From 1950 to 1960, 236,000 whites and 10,142 Negroes moved into the corridor while outside the corridor the state had a net migration loss of 145,500 whites and 71,546 Negroes. Between 1940 and 1950, 81 percent of Virginia's population growth was in the corridor; from 1950 to 1960, 91 percent.

## The Slums and the Problem of Urban Congestion

Present problems of urban congestion, exemplified in the great megalopolitan strips, go beyond the dimensions of increasing density, as serious as this may become. Congestion affects the quality of environment and of the population itself. People who once made an acceptable adjustment to a simple agriculture—one which no longer exists as a going concern—move to cities and face adjustment to a complex environment. Since Virginia is entering this transition ahead of many Southern states, it will be helpful to glance at urban structure as it is now developing. Cities grow around central business districts in something resembling a series of circles. Here the trend is toward decentralization by reason of the growth on the urban periphery of new shopping centers which can furnish parking areas for retail trade. This movement is clearly related to the growth of rings of city suburbs which is treated later in this essay.

The central problems of urban congestion and substandard environment are tied up with those areas which we have come to call "city slums." Slums can be defined as areas which specialize in providing substandard accommodations to those who cannot make an adequate adjustment to city life. People who are pushed out of agriculture approach the city more or less as rural refugees, entering the lowest level of urban rents and services. Typically these are areas, not of second-hand housing but of tenth- and twentieth-hand housing. Typically also, the slums are ringed around the central business district and represent, as

---

[3] In addition to the metropolitan areas, three subregions are involved: the Northern Piedmont (4 counties), Fall Line area (4 counties), and the York Peninsula (4 counties). They had a population of 326,382, mainly rural and small town (Lorin A. Thompson, "Recent Population Changes in Virginia," *ibid.*, Feb. 15, 1961.

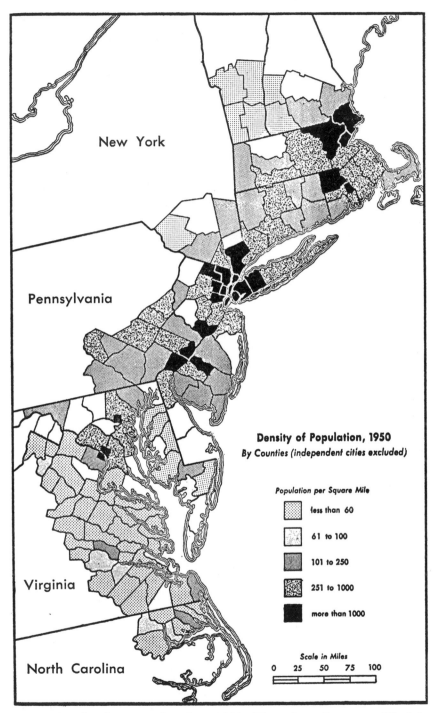

*VI. Megalopolis, general outline, 1950.* (*From Jean Gottmann,* Virginia
at Mid-Century, © *1955 by Henry Holt and Company, Inc., New York.*)

it were, the port of arrival of the less-fortunate migrants. Dilapidated housing is not repaired because in the natural course of expansion business concerns will occupy these run-down residential areas. In Northern cities such areas have received successive waves of foreign immigrants, and many have now become Black Belts harboring a displaced Negro peasantry from the South. Virginia lacks the foreign component in its slums, but its place is taken by the poor-white farmers and the Negro families whose opportunities in the new environment remain restricted by their lack of education and urban skills. In these areas are found the problems of poverty, delinquency, and unemployment which make the slums the slums. This remains true for the area, for as fast as families can improve their standards and living conditions they desert the slums to occupy better neighborhoods. The continuation of slums is then to be explained in part by the continued migration to cities of people who hope to "better themselves."

Slums, however, are not to be explained by any one factor; they represent the convergence of many conditions of inadequacy, those which exist among the people as well as those in their environment. No over-all solution appears to be in sight, and considered from this point of view the wonder is not that urban slums continue to exist. The puzzle, in fact, is that they do not expand at a faster rate to disable more of the oncoming generation than they do. It must be kept in mind that at no time do a majority of slum dwellers fail to receive an education, take to delinquency, or even land on the welfare rolls. In short, dwellers in city slums are not outcasts or rebels against society; they are more often a working-class group of the less skilled. Individual improvement, as we have said, does not improve slums; individuals who achieve simply leave these areas for better neighborhoods. Only if the stream of poor migrants to the cities were to stop, could the city draw its breath and face up to the problem of urban renewal. Even then our real-estate interests would be faced with the question, To whom do we rent our substandard housing? The other side of the coin is found in the suburbs, which represent largely middle-class groups of skilled, white-collar workers and the business and professional classes. We shall discuss this later in the essay.

## The Suburban Trend

Virginia's urban strip development, bending eastward to the coast as it does, stands in notable contrast to major population growth in the rest of the Southeast. Here the great advance in industrialization and urbanization has occurred along the Piedmont Crescent, paralleling the Southern Railway—the South's "Golden Street"—as it curves south and westward through the Carolinas and Georgia, ending at Birmingham. The northern end of the Crescent can be located in Virginia, beginning at its upper point in the Lynchburg metropolitan area and passing through Danville.

Coastal areas in North Carolina, and to some extent those of South Carolina and Georgia, resemble dead-end territory when compared to Tidewater Virginia with its development. Virginia of the early colonial settlement holds its rural people better, and some of its suburban settlement is now devoted to restoring old mansions.

What feeds this pattern of increasing settlement and how does the settlement spread? It requires more than the analysis of density patterns to explain this.

People who are moving urbanward to participate in the center work of our economy no longer find it necessary to live in the urban core of metropolitan centers. The metropolitan trend is generating a new migration—a movement out of the inner city into its fringes. Every large American city is now surrounded by rings of suburbs. So great is this trend in certain parts of the country that the suburban dweller who moves out in search of green trees and grass finds that he has run out of open country. Real-estate developers creating new subdivisions are beginning to find that the suburbs of one metropolitan center thrust into the suburbs of the next.

Virginia is participating in this multiplicity of changes, a kind of threefold movement as I see it, in which certain shifts swallow up the effects of others. For this reason it will not be safe for those who view the metropolitan trend as all-encompassing to predict the depopulation of rural areas. Urbanization and metropolitan movements are now serving to repopulate certain rural areas. First, agricultural areas give up their population to feed the movement into cities, leaving the land to be consolidated into mechanized farming for controlled markets. The population moves into the central core of settlement in our cities. This trend cannot long continue, however, because in its second stage the urban core passes its optimum density and proceeds to expand. The third trend, the suburbanization movement, passes far beyond the city limits and proceeds to repopulate contiguous rural areas standing in the path of suburban expansion. Thus it appears that Virginia's rural counties in the corridor will gradually be repopulated. Note, for example, how four-lane highways between two cities draw open-country settlement. All this is hastened by the population explosion, in which the middle classes, having decided to do their duty by posterity, now have four children instead of two.

It is hardly necessary to describe our suburbs. They are populated by a homogeneous middle class whose values have been inimitably put by a popular song which states that the houses and children all look alike, the children all go to the university, and all are made of "tickey-tackey." Virginia has retained certain values of rural life from its early settlement, and the fine custom of restoring old homes and watching boxwood grow obviously reduces the amount of tickey-tackey. The cutting edge of the suburban movement has been called the "rural-urban fringe," the initial phase that represents the city taking over the countryside. It also represents the "I'd rather do it myself" aspect of the suburban movement. Out beyond the developers, who are continually laying out new settlements and counting up the profits inherent in subdividing farms into residential lots, these new pioneers move in. As shock troops of the rural-urban fringe, they take advantage of rural electrification, of oil-heating systems and septic tanks, to settle down among the farmers. Such a pioneer begins by putting his children on the bus and sending them to a consolidated rural school; his wife engages a butter-and-egg man to deliver produce at home. In the end it costs just as much as it did to live in town and pay city taxes, but the new homesteader could not have known that in the beginning.

Finally the farmers give up the struggle, sell out to the subdividers, move away, and join the urban job hunt. The farmers' daughters and sons are now attending the urban high school with its social functions. The rural-urban fringe has accomplished its transformation and is simply another suburb—inconveniently located further out. Parents either drive the youngsters into the city now for necessary social functions, or they buy the second and third car demanded by the children of the affluent society. Such is the confluence of suburbanization and the population explosion in Virginia's changing population density.

4

# Virginia's Blue-Collar Workers

*Lorin A. Thompson, Director*

*Bureau of Population and Economic Research*

*University of Virginia*

Blue-collar workers have contributed much to the development of Virginia and the nation. Their proportion of the labor force is influenced by the stage of technology of their society and its pattern of urban and rural residence. Changes in technology have been accompanied by a smaller portion of the total labor force engaging in agriculture, forestry, and fishing; mining; manufacturing; and construction. Persons engaged in such activities comprise a far smaller proportion of the total labor force today than they did in previous years. In the year 1820 about 88 percent of all persons engaged in occupational pursuits were in agriculture.[1] By 1840 this percentage had dropped to about 82; by 1880, to 51.5; by 1890, to 49; by 1900, to 45.5; by 1940, to 25.4; by 1950, to 15.1; and by 1960, to 7.8. Similarly, in the United States as a whole as it existed in 1820, 82 percent of all persons engaged in the various occupational pursuits were in agriculture. Sixty years later, in 1880, 47.5 percent were engaged in agriculture; in 1900, 35.5 percent; and in 1960, 6.7 percent. Since 1960 the employment trend in agriculture has still been downward, and it appears to be approaching an irreducible minimum. In Virginia in 1960 the proportion of workers employed in agriculture was a little less then 8 percent, only slightly higher than in the nation as a whole.

Occupational changes during the past century and a half reflect the dramatic changes in the way of life as well as in the economic organization of society. Until quite recently living on a farm was both a way of life and a means of livelihood. The continuous application of scientific knowledge and technology to agriculture has largely transformed farming from a way of life into a commercial enterprise. It has become popular to speak of farming as "agribusiness" and agriculture as an "industry." The ramifications and the implications of these developments extend into all facets of our life. A brief review of some of these changes follows.

In 1900 about two-thirds of all those employed in the United States were engaged in agriculture, mining, manufacturing, and construction, and about 30 percent were engaged in service occupations. In 1960 the

[1] U.S. Bureau of the Census, *U.S. Census of Population: 1960* and earlier decades. All figures quoted, unless otherwise specified, were taken or derived from the relevant *Census of Population.*

proportion engaged in agriculture, manufacturing, construction, and mining was about 35 percent. Such changes have occurred as the result of the development and application of science and technology to the aforementioned areas of production. Large investments in machinery and mechanical equipment have been necessary to provide new and modern tools of production.

A hundred years ago comparatively little mechanical energy was used in agriculture. Motive power was produced by animals and men. At the turn of this century new implements and machinery were being introduced to farming. These developments can be illustrated simply by comparing the number of tractors versus horses and mules on Virginia farms between 1880 and 1960.[2] From 1880 until 1920 there were about 170 horses and mules per 1,000 population. In 1920 there was 1 tractor per 1,000 people. By 1960 the tractors had increased to 23.4 per 1,000 people, and horses and mules had declined from 178 per 1,000 in 1920 to 21 per 1,000. According to the *Census of Agriculture* there were some 410,000 horses and mules in Virginia in 1920—the highest number on record—and in forty years this number had declined to 84,300. In 1920 there were a few less than 2,400 tractors on farms and in 1960 there were 92,351. Between 1950 and 1960 the number of tractors on farms increased from 48,000 to 92,351, and the number of horses and mules declined from 205,000 to 84,300. The number of tractors almost doubled while the number of horses and mules dropped in 1960 to less than half the number in 1950.

*Developments Since 1940*

The industrial composition or structure of employment in Virginia has changed sharply in a period of twenty years. In 1940, 54 percent of all employed workers were engaged in agriculture, mining, construction, and manufacturing—often grouped and spoken of as the "production industries." By 1950 this percentage had dropped to 45; and by 1960, to 38.5. This development closely follows the pattern of the nation, in which the opportunities for employment depend more and more upon the expansion of the service industries. Changes in the industrial composition of the economy have much to do with the kinds of jobs available in each industry. Traditionally we have thought of blue-collar jobs as those related to agriculture, mining, manufacturing, and construction. It is clear that the proportion of those employed in the four areas of production has been shrinking. This shrinkage is inversely proportional

---

[2] U.S. Bureau of the Census, *U.S. Census of Agriculture*, various years.

to the rate at which technological improvements are introduced into the various sectors of the economy. The blue-collar worker has been society's producer of goods and equipment. Fewer workers with the aid of machines can now produce in such abundance that our ability to provide employment for all people is related to the growth and expansion of the many sectors in the service economy.

Changes in the structure of the economy have also been associated with the residential pattern of the population as a whole. The number of people living in the open country in Virginia outside of towns of more than 1,000 has not changed greatly since 1900. Persons living in the open country, including some living in small towns of less than 2,500, whether engaged in agricultural pursuits or in some other activity are classified by the United States Census Bureau as rural population. In 1900 the rural population excluding these townspeople of Virginia was 1,429,000. In 1960 the number was 1,596,000, an increase of about 12 percent in the sixty years. In 1900, however, the rural population as just defined included 77 percent of the state's total population and in 1960, about 40 percent of the total. These figures illustrate the shift in the pattern of residence from rural to urban areas. The increasing urbanism in our society has brought many new problems. Urban planners currently are considering the various ways in which the design of urban areas can encourage and promote a good life as well as provide convenient physical facilities. Such leading architects and students of planning as Edward Durell Stone and the late Frank Lloyd Wright have commented on the ugliness of our cities.[3] As the urban population continues to increase, the kinds of plans and designs for living will determine whether our cities become even uglier or whether they provide beauty along with the necessary physical facilities and cultural amenities.

A more complete picture of recent social and economic changes comes from examining in some detail the variations in the patterns of change among the whites and nonwhites in the rural and urban areas of the state during the past thirty years. Between 1930 and 1960 the white rural population in Virginia increased from about 1,200,000 to 1,375,000, or 15 percent. The corresponding change among the nonwhites was from 437,500 to 387,000, a decline of 12 percent. On the other hand, the urban population in both races increased rapidly during the last thirty years: the urban Negroes from about 214,000 in 1930 to 438,000 in 1960, or 105 percent; the urban whites from 572,000 to 1,767,000, or 208 percent. These differential rates of growth are related to the kinds of occupational opportunities open to the two races.

---

[3] Frank Lloyd Wright, *The Living City* (New York, 1958), p. 11.

*Blue-Collar Occupations in a Changing Society*

To assess the direction of future development it is useful to examine closely the changes in the opportunities for employment of blue-collar workers in the state in recent years. Blue-collar workers include the following census classifications: craftsmen, foremen and kindred workers; operatives and kindred workers; private household workers; service workers except private household, which include protective service workers such as bailiffs, firemen, policemen, and the like; waiters, cooks, and bartenders, and other service workers that are employed in amusement places, boarding and lodging places, and hotels. This group also includes such occupations as elevator operators, hairdressers, housekeepers and stewards, kitchen workers, practical nurses, and the like. Among the laborers included in the blue-collar group are farm laborers, farm foremen, and other laborers involved in construction, manufacturing, warehousing, and so on.

Significant changes in the employment of blue-collar workers have occurred. First, since 1930 the number of blue-collar workers has changed little; some parts of the total group have increased, other parts have declined, and the group as a whole has become a smaller share of total employment. During this same period white-collar and related professional employment has increased in number and as a share of the total. In Virginia blue-collar jobs represented about 60 percent of all employment in 1940. Ten years later, in 1950, this share had dropped to 56 percent; by 1960, to 51 percent. Interesting differences have occurred in the employment of whites and nonwhites. In 1940, 49.5 percent of all employed white workers were in blue-collar occupations; the corresponding percentage among the nonwhites was 82. By 1950, 49 percent of the whites were in blue-collar occupations and 81 percent of the nonwhites; in 1960 the corresponding percentages were 43.5 and 78. These figures indicate clearly that Negroes in Virginia have not moved into white-collar or professional jobs in any great numbers. Some of the factors which may be related to these differences will be explored later.

Blue-collar workers may be divided conveniently into five occupational groups. The most skilled group consists of craftsmen, foremen, and kindred workers. The classification covers skills used in all forms of construction and repair work as well as in specialized work in manufacturing plants. In 1960 there were about 177,500 craftsmen, representing 13.3 percent of the total number of employed persons. In 1950 craftsmen represented 13.2 percent, and in 1940, 10.4 percent. This group increased by 62 percent between 1940 and 1950, but the increase has tapered off to 16.8 percent during the past decade. Employment in the skilled crafts has been confined largely to males; only about 2.5 percent of skilled workers are females. In 1960, 16,400 or 9.2 percent of all skilled craftsmen employed in Virginia were Negroes.

Another occupational group closely related to the craftsman group is that of operative and kindred workers. Operatives engage in the same general occupations and industries as craftsmen, although the degree of skill required is somewhat less. One of the important differences between operatives and craftsmen is the fact that the operatives are familiar with fewer machines. The total number of operatives in Virginia increased 42 percent between 1940 and 1950 and by about 4 percent between 1950 and 1960. Employment of the more diversified skilled craftsmen has increased fairly rapidly while the number of operatives has increased relatively little. By 1960 Negroes held 22.2 percent of the jobs in the operative group—a proportion similar to their total number in the population. The largest increase in this group of occupations occurred between 1940 and 1950, when the increase among the Negroes was 83 percent, 33 percent for the whites, and 42 percent for all groups.

Domestic employment as household servants has declined sharply. In 1960 domestic service accounted for about 1.6 percent of the total number employed. The erosion of such employment took place during the 1930's. As other occupational opportunities opened up, increasing numbers of people previously engaged in domestic employment sought other occupations.

Many of the service workers classified by the Census Bureau as "other" service workers are employed in specialized institutions. In addition, this group includes people engaged in protective services such as firemen and policemen and other forms of personal service. Between 1940 and 1950 employment in the "other" service group of occupations increased by 78 percent; between 1950 and 1960 the increase was about 16 percent. About 10 percent of all employed Negroes were so engaged, and they represented about 45 percent of the total number of persons engaged in such work.

The reduction in the number of farm laborers in Virginia has been most dramatic. In 1940 about 87,000 persons were listed as farm laborers; in 1950 this number dropped to 57,000, which was 66 percent of the number in 1940; and by 1960 this group had declined further to 39,600, or 36 percent of the number in 1940. This decline, I suspect, is a further effect of the increase in the number of farm tractors and the decrease in the number of horses and mules. The proportionate decline in Negro farm laborers between 1940 and 1960 was as great as among the whites. Negro farm laborers in 1960 represented about 36 percent of the number who were so engaged in 1940. Among the whites the corresponding figure was 37 percent. The decrease in the number of horses and mules and of farm laborers is a further illustration of the substitution of mechanical energy for human and animal energy.

*Changes by Color and Sex*

The foregoing discussion has highlighted the proportion of whites and Negroes engaged in blue-collar occupations. It is of equal interest to examine the number and proportion of white and colored females participating in the blue-collar occupations. First, the changes during the last twenty years in the number of women engaged in the several groups of blue-collar workers will be examined.

Between 1940 and 1950 the number of white women in Virginia in the craftsman occupation group increased from 1,253 to 4,329. This was an increase of 174 percent. Between 1950 and 1960 the percentage increase was 16.9. Total employment of white females between 1950 and 1960 increased by 52 percent. The entrance of women into the occupation group designated craftsmen burgeoned during the decade 1940 to 1950 but slacked off between 1950 and 1960. The proportion of Negro women in these occupations increased percentagewise somewhat faster than did that of the whites, but by 1960 Negroes comprised only about one-eighth of the females employed as craftsmen.

Among the operatives that are employed in many manufacturing and production industries the increase in the number of white females engaged in such occupations was 40 percent between 1940 and 1950 and 24 percent between 1950 and 1960. The corresponding percentages for Negro females were 48.4 and 4.5. In 1950 a little over 20 percent of the female operatives were Negroes. Perhaps the labor shortage existing during World War II opened doors to Negro women at a rate which was not maintained once the demand for such workers declined.

The employment of private household workers has changed sharply in the last several decades. In Virginia and the nation this decrease began in the 1930's. In Virginia the males represented a little less than 4 percent of the total persons employed in private household occupations in 1960 as compared with 6.6 percent in 1940. Total employment of females in this occupation group was about 55,700 in 1940 and declined to 41.700 in 1950, then increased to about 49,000 in 1960. One interesting pattern is that the number of white females in private household occupations in 1940 was 10,664; this number dropped to 6,138 in 1950 and rose again to 10,745 in 1960. Among Negro females a somewhat similar movement was observed in that the number in 1940 was 45,000, in 1950 35,600, and in 1960 38,150. Opportunities for employment in household domestic service may be on the increase. The demand for such workers seems to be brisk, and the number of qualified people interested in such occupations is somewhat less than the demand. The demand for all types of service employment has risen sharply as the need for production workers tends to decline with the advance of modern technology. It is difficult to tell whether this slight increase in employment between 1950 and 1960 will continue, but the opportunity for expansion of such employment seems to be good. Seventy-eight percent of the persons engaged in private household occupations were colored females and 22 percent were white.

The number of "other" service workers employed in hotels, motels, and service establishments has increased substantially between 1940 and 1960. With 1940 as a base for this group of occupations, employment between 1940 and 1960 among the four color and sex groups increased as follows: all males by 106 percent, white males by 235 percent, and Negro males by 40 percent; all females by 170 percent, white females by 154 percent, and Negro females by 194 percent. In this group of occupations Negro males represented about 45 percent of total males and Negro females about 41 percent of all females. Negroes were employed in much larger proportion in this group of service occupations than their share of the total population. Service employment in institutions has absorbed many of the people formerly employed as household domestics. For example, in 1940 household work and other service work together provided jobs for 103,426 people; in 1960, for 152,223, an increase of 48 percent. These two service groups in 1940 accounted for 11.5 percent of all workers; in 1960, for about 11.4 percent. In 1940 there were 60,400 household workers in the state, or 6.8 percent of the total employed. In 1960 the number of household workers was about 51,000, or 3.8 percent of the total number employed. The total number of persons in the service occupations themselves increased from about 43,000 to 101,500 during the twenty-year period. This was an increase of 135 percent. The internal shifts within this group of service occupations during the last two decades reflect the increasingly institutional character of such employment.

The need for full-time domestic servants in households has been modified by the increasing use of automatic washers, dryers, dishwashers, and other automatic appliances. The requirement that the householder pay social security taxes on people earning as much as $50 in any quarter probably discourages some from the employment of domestics. There is also a growing practice by which the householder contracts with an employer who has people who will perform household work, and the contractor takes care of the tax payments. The need for part-time and occasional employment is being met in many places by the organization of contract employers who furnish household workers, secretaries, bookkeepers, and the like for limited periods of time for a contract price. The trends with respect to household employment do not indicate at this time that any rapid increase will occur. The United States Department of Labor[4] has initiated a program to encourage more women to train for service occupations in the home.

As has been pointed out, the occupational groups which have suffered the greatest declines in the last twenty years are farm laborers. Employment among the other common labor groups which include mining, construction, and related occupations has also declined. These workers are mostly males, and the decline in numbers between 1940 and 1960 was about 15 percent. If farm laborers and other laborers are taken together, their numbers dropped from 181,705 in 1940 to 102,794 in 1960. In 1940 the various labor groups represented about 20 percent of the total number of people employed; in 1960 this percentage had declined to 7.7. This development shows, as few other things do, the rapidly changing character of our society. Before the days of machinery and technology laborers as a group were in demand on the farms, in construction, and in manufacturing operations. Their relative numbers have shrunk with the advent of machinery and advanced technology.

*Implications for Social Policy*

The changes in the structure of employment that have occurred at an increased tempo raise a number of important questions of economic and social policy. Among the more pressing matters is how to develop and provide employment opportunities in such number and kind as to enable the increasing number of youth to find opportunities to support themselves and build a career that will be personally satisfying and socially useful. This becomes more difficult in view of the rapidity with which scientific and technological change alters the job structure of manufacturing, mining, agriculture, and construction. Technology and automation are finding useful applications in the service industries, such as transportation and communication; wholesaling and retailing; banking, finance, and business services. The adoption and use of new methods tend to improve the quality of service and to reduce costs. Such improvements have greatly expanded the need for new capital and the opportunities for investment.

A second group of factors is demographic. The contributions of

[4] Jean A. Wells, "Training Women and Girls for Work," *Occupational Outlook Quarterly*, vol. 4 (1960).

research in the physical and biological sciences as they have been applied to the treatment and control of disease have reduced death rates, thus increasing the rate of population growth and lengthening the life span.

The applications of scientific knowledge to the production of goods and services have enabled us to raise more food and fiber with fewer workers, to manufacture more goods at lower unit costs with fewer workers, and to mine more coal and minerals with fewer workers. The technological improvements which have resulted in rapid obsolescence of jobs and skills pose challenges with respect to finding suitable employment for an increasing labor force. This in turn raises questions with regard to education. How much education, for whom, and for what?

## *Education, the Worker, and the Future*

In the foregoing sections of this paper I have shown the sharp decline in the importance of blue-collar workers in our society. A most persistent question is whether or not more education for more of our people is the answer to the dilemma of the blue-collar worker. As an exercise in logic let us assume that the proportion of blue-collar workers in the labor force of Virginia continues to decline from its current level of 50 percent to 25 percent. This can only be accomplished by increased applications of technology in which machines are substituted for men. Can this decline in blue-collar workers be offset by an expansion of white-collar, technical, professional, and other occupations? Is it feasible and possible to solve this problem by providing new and different kinds of training for the displaced blue-collar workers? Will the demand for their services be commensurate with the supply of new workers so trained? How rapidly will the jobs in the non-blue-collar occupations expand, change, and become obsolete?

These questions are not answered easily. Indeed, we are uncertain of the ways and means by which reasonable solutions to these problems may be found. Yet we must seek answers which are consonant with our ideals of a good society. It seems clear that one of the problems is the rapidity of current change in occupational structure. In certain areas it is difficult to train enough people well enough and soon enough to meet the demands of our times. Scientists, mathematicians, and linear programmers are examples. In other areas workers and machines alike are quickly obsolete. The machine can be scrapped but not the worker. Displaced workers in agriculture, mining, and manufacturing illustrate this aspect of the contemporary situation.

Contemporary society makes much of status symbols. Blue-collar positions have long been regarded as ranging from the bottom to about halfway up the scale in the social hierarchy. Among some of the characteristics used to determine the relative position of individuals in various occupational pursuits have been the amount of education needed, the degree of skill required to perform satisfactorily, the relative scarcity or abundance of qualifications for performing in an occupation as related to the market demand, and the prevailing rates of pay. These and other elements in various combinations and proportions (not necessarily uniform or constant in their application) provide the measuring devices for status.

In our appraisal of the importance of any given kind of work there is a strong tendency to confuse the status of the occupation of the worker with the real benefit to a business concern, an organization, or society. The result of failure of any essential part of an engine is well known. Nonperformance may result from the malfunction of a very small part just as easily as from that of a large one. The dilemmas of shortages of people to perform essential and useful work in the midst of labor surpluses and relatively high rates of unemployment in part are the results of false standards of status.

Comparisons of educational level with levels in the occupational hierarchy and income show that the amount of education is directly related to the level attained in the hierarchy of occupations and the amount of income received. The familiar logic of the day is that the more education the better the chances of attaining a prestige position and high income. This is not quite as crass as it sounds. Occupations which require extensive knowledge and skill require long periods of time in preparation. This involves an investment of money and time. Individuals with twelve years of education at age eighteen represent one level of capital investment; those with seven or eight additional years of education represent a much larger capital investment. If the ability level of each were the same, the expected level of earnings would be proportional to the amount of education. Ability levels, however, are generally not the same. The level of education is strongly influenced by the ability and capacity of the individual. Extended exposure of individuals with limited capacity to the processes of higher or technical education is often disappointing both to the persons being educated and to those sponsoring the education. The proposition that more education is the solution to differences in occupational level and income is only partially true.

The 1960 census provides a great deal of information about the characteristics of the population. Among the more interesting are the data on educational level, income, and residence class—urban and rural. Table 3 summarizes several interesting items dealing with the differences in education and income of the urban and rural population of Virginia. The items in the table are the median years of school completed for the population twenty-five years old and over, median family income, and the median income of males and females with income. The residential classifications in the table include the total urban population; the population of the urbanized areas, which include the central cities and the urban fringe; other urban population, which includes people living in cities of 10,000 or more and in places of from 2,500 to 10,000; the total rural population; and the rural farm population.

TABLE 3. SELECTED CHARACTERISTICS OF THE URBAN AND RURAL POPULATION OF VIRGINIA, 1960

| Area and class | Median years of school completed 25 yrs. & over | Median income of | | |
|---|---|---|---|---|
| | | Families | Males with income | Females with income |
| The state | 9.9 | $4,964 | $3,250 | $1,232 |
| Total urban | 11.5 | 5,920 | 4,042 | 1,470 |
| Urbanized area | 11.8 | 6,211 | 4,220 | 1,562 |
| Central city | 10.5 | 5,208 | 3,428 | 1,316 |
| Fringe | 12.4 | 7,667 | 5,488 | 2,202 |
| Other urban—Total | 10.0 | 5,082 | 3,422 | 1,258 |
| Places of 10,000 & over | 10.0 | 5,222 | 3,493 | 1,318 |
| Places 2,500 10,000 | 10.2 | 4,895 | 3,326 | 1,157 |
| Rural—Total | 8.0 | 3,791 | 2,372 | 886 |
| Rural farm | 7.6 | 2,714 | 1,573 | 683 |

*Source:* U.S. Bureau of the Census, *U.S. Census of Population: 1960, Virginia*, Tables 70, 71.

The median years of schooling completed range from 7.6 for the rural farm population to 12.4 for residents of the urban fringe. The levels of median family income and the income of males and females with income are much lower in the rural farm areas than in the several groups of urban areas. The educational level of the rural population twenty-five years old and over is also lower than that of the urban groups.

In recent decades there has been continued improvement in the amount of schooling of all sectors of the population of the state. Currently the children in rural areas are attending school as long as those in urban places so that differences noted in the past will disappear within this generation. The economic organization of large cities, small cities, the urban fringe, and the rural farm areas is, however, less likely to change rapidly. The differences in income level found in urban and rural areas reflect the occupational pattern of the people living in these areas. In 1959 the median income of male blue-collar workers ranged from

$882 for private household workers to $4,596 for craftsmen. In the non-blue-collar occupations which include the white-collar and professional groups, the corresponding median earnings for males ranged from $1,414 for farmers and farm managers to $6,798 for professional and kindred workers. The median earnings for females engaged in these occupations differed sharply from those of the males. The median incomes for females in the blue-collar group ranged from a low of $574 for farm laborers to $2,610 for those classified as craftsmen and kindred workers. In the white-collar and professional groups the median incomes ranged from $722 for farmers and farm managers to $3,494 for professional and kindred workers. The differences in income received by those engaging in the different kinds of occupations reflect to a very large extent the prevailing practices in the market place for labor. The extent to which these differentials are related to the relative demand for workers in blue-collar occupations and to the amount and kind of education the worker has completed is not entirely clear.

### Blue-Collar Workers and the Good Society

In building a good society it is desirable to relate economic differentials to political and moral ideals. A society which emphasizes status and income level as the dominant social values tends to minimize the importance of job satisfaction and creative effort. The values given top priority in a society tend to shape the organization of its economy and political system. The broad trends reviewed above indicate that the blue-collar workers as a group have been declining in relative importance, and this trend may be expected to continue. It is also true, however, that there are individual occupations within the broad class in which the demand and social need are much greater than the supply. These are mainly in the fields of personal service. The difficulties of training a sufficient number of people to meet these shortages are compounded by the fact that blue-collar jobs have been regarded as lowly and menial occupations.[5] The persons who have engaged in these occupations have often found that, no matter how well they do their work, acceptable social status is not attained. Failure to recognize the value of the contribution which many of the blue-collar workers make to the social order has also tended to keep the wage levels down. This situation represents one of the challenges of the future.

The declining importance of many blue-collar occupations, together with increases and declines among the white-collar occupations, presents a challenge to education. In our rapidly changing society with its

[5] Vance Packard, *The Status Seekers* (New York, 1959).

advancing technology, colleges and universities have been hard put to keep up with the demand for specialists in a great variety of fields. The prospect is that this demand will continue for some time to come. The kind and quality of education which would be most profitable to many of the blue-collar workers need attention. Many blue-collar workers engage in occupations which do not require great amounts of specialized or intensive education, and many do not require complex skill. Each of the occupations, however, expects dependability in the performance of the task no matter how simple. The fact that the task is not complex does not mean that it is not important.

One of the hard truths that society learns from the ravages of strikes is that the workers in an individual occupation, even though not numerous, can bring about chaos and collapse of the whole economy. The thrust of these remarks is to emphasize the point that all jobs are important and that plant failure, social inconvenience, and disruption can occur from poor performance or lack of performance on the part of any group that is a part of an operation. Failure to recognize the importance of individual contributions and denial of appropriate recognition and status to qualified people are the source of much of our present social friction. How can some of these basic problems be resolved?

Education is not governed by any single narrow goal and should not be. If we are to improve the career prospects for the youth of today, it seems clear that education should offer more diversified training for many of our people. Reference has been made to the rapid rates of change in the demand for people in various occupations. It has also been pointed out that shortages of qualified workers in many occupations exist at the same time that many people are unemployed or underemployed. These two facts, if put together, suggest that education should acquaint the children more thoroughly with many of the occupations and heritages of the past and should provide more ample opportunities for training in the manual and creative arts. These are the foundations of occupational skills and crafts. Familiarity with tools and methods of construction enables people to improve their standard of living by transforming raw materials into desired objects. Expansion of the do-it-yourself idea, not only as a form of recreation and diversion but as an important area of education, would be desirable. More school training in the arts and crafts would prepare more of our young people to cope more adequately with the changes which are apt to confront them. Improvement would come if accomplishment were the basis of social recognition rather than conspicuous consumption. Blue-collar workers may be a smaller proportion of the total labor force in the future than in the past but they certainly will be no less important.

5

# Skills, Training, and Education of Virginia's White-Collar Workers

*William Hugh McFarlane*

*Formerly Director*

*State Council of Higher Education*

*Richmond, Virginia*

The substantial changes that are taking place in the levels of skill required of Virginia's labor force are a significant factor often overlooked in recurrent discussions of the state's ongoing transition from a rural, agricultural economy to an urban, industrial economy. By 1960, for example, over 40 percent of all employed workers in Virginia held white-collar jobs, whereas in 1950 only 33.6 percent had jobs so classified. Of the 190,000-plus jobs gained by the Virginia economy during the fifties, over 80 percent were white-collar.

The gains recorded by Virginia in manufacturing and service employment between 1950 and 1960 tell the story. The type of manufacturing which has expanded in the state, together with industry-wide technological changes, has created heavy demands for professional, technical, supervisory, and other nonproduction workers. With urbanization has come higher income levels and rapid expansion of service industry, where 60 percent of all employment is in the white-collar categories, as compared with 40 percent in other industries.

As Virginia's industrial employment adjusts to comparable national patterns, the supporting role of the state's educational system becomes more important to economic growth. The formal educational training of the typical white-collar worker exceeds four years of college at professional and technical levels; in other categories it averages more than four years of high school. A new breed of worker called the "technician" is in heavy demand to relieve highly trained professionals of the routine work in the economy.

Virginia's educational system is not yet fully geared to meet the new demands being placed upon it. Vocational training at the secondary level has continued to emphasize blue-collar skills in spite of declining employment opportunities. The importance of skill training at the postsecondary level has not yet been adequately recognized. Public and private colleges in Virginia are limited in their capacity to absorb enrollment increases and to develop rapidly the expanded programs and services that the booming Virginia economy requires. Most discouraging of all are the undernourished, competitive, and scattered efforts to provide a first-rate program of graduate training and research, particularly in scientific and technological fields.

Some progress is recorded in bringing the educational system more up to date. In the end, however, the effectiveness of the changeover will be determined by the kind of commitment Virginia's people are willing to make toward providing an educational system that is adequate to the promise of Virginia's future.

## Virginia's Employment Trends, 1950–60

Recent employment trends show heavier demands for white-collar workers than for any other category and indicate generally that Virginia's employment patterns are rapidly adjusting to national ones. Growth of demands for white-collar workers in manufacturing and service has been, and will probably continue to be, a mainstay of the Virginia economy. Minor growth occurred in construction at approximately the same rate as

TABLE 4. DISTRIBUTION OF EMPLOYMENT, BY INDUSTRY AND OCCUPATION, UNITED STATES AND VIRGINIA, 1950–60

|  | Virginia | | United States | |
|---|---|---|---|---|
|  | 1950 | 1960 | 1950 | 1960 |
| *Industry** |  |  |  |  |
| Service | 52.9% | 58.4% | 52.3% | 55.3% |
| Manufacturing | 20.6 | 22.6 | 26.0 | 27.1 |
| Agriculture | 14.6 | 6.6 | 12.2 | 7.4 |
| Construction | 7.2 | 6.1 | 6.1 | 5.9 |
| Mining | 2.5 | 1.4 | 1.7 | 1.0 |
| Forestry & fishing | 0.4 | 0.4 | 2.2 | 1.4 |
| *Occupation* |  |  |  |  |
| Prof., tech., & kindred | 8.3 | 11.5 | 8.7 | 11.2 |
| Managerial | 7.8 | 7.9 | 8.9 | 8.4 |
| Clerical & kindred | 11.2 | 14.0 | 12.3 | 14.4 |
| Sales | 6.3 | 7.0 | 6.9 | 7.2 |
| Total white-collar | 33.6 | 40.4 | 36.8 | 41.2 |
| Total other | 66.4 | 59.6 | 63.2 | 58.8 |

*Sources: Virginia Economic Review,* July 1963, and U.S. Bureau of the Census, *U.S. Census of Population: 1960.*

* Excludes industry not reported.

in the nation. Agriculture and mining continued to decline. Table 4 shows relative changes for the state and nation between 1950 and 1960. These demonstrate that much larger adjustments have taken place in the state than in the nation in all industrial and occupational categories except forestry and fishing.

Virginia now exceeds national levels of employment in service-type industry and in the employment of professional, technical, and kindred workers. It lags significantly behind the nation in manufacturing employment and slightly behind in over-all employment of white-collar workers, but in both instances it has been rapidly overtaking the national economy.

Of the 190,710 net increase in jobs which developed in the Virginia economy during the fifties, 156,014 were in white-collar categories, 82 percent of the total. Almost 80 percent of these white-collar jobs were in the professional, technical, and kindred subgroup (58,686) and in clerical fields (59,902).

Table 5 shows that most of the 156,000-plus increase in white-collar jobs occurred in service and manufacturing industry. The increase in

TABLE 5. CHANGE AND DISTRIBUTION OF OCCUPATIONAL EMPLOYMENT FOR SERVICE AND MANUFACTURING INDUSTRIES, VIRGINIA, 1950–60

| Industry & occupation | Increase 1950–60 | Pct. increase | Pct. of total empl. | |
|---|---|---|---|---|
| | | | 1960 | 1950 |
| *Service* | 170,989 | 28.0 | 100.0 | 100.0 |
| Prof., tech. & kindred | 48,569 | 58.7 | 16.8 | 13.6 |
| Managerial | 11,944 | 16.6 | 10.9 | 12.0 |
| Clerical | 48,234 | 44.8 | 19.9 | 17.6 |
| Sales | 15,896 | 23.9 | 10.5 | 10.9 |
| Total white-collar | 124,643 | 37.7 | 58.1 | 54.1 |
| Total other | 46,346 | 16.5 | 41.9 | 45.9 |
| *Manufacturing* | 64,434 | 27.4 | 100.0 | 100.0 |
| Prof., tech. & kindred | 9,087 | 119.6 | 5.6 | 3.2 |
| Managerial | 2,692 | 30.2 | 3.9 | 3.8 |
| Clerical | 10,415 | 64.2 | 8.9 | 6.9 |
| Sales | 5,354 | 92.3 | 3.7 | 2.5 |
| Total white-collar | 27,548 | 71.5 | 22.1 | 16.4 |
| Total other | 36,886 | 18.7 | 79.8* | 83.6 |

*Source: Va. Econ. Rev.,* July 1963, Appendix.

\* Because of rounding the total here is not 100 percent.

white-collar employment relative to total employment in these fields should also be noted.

During the past five years manufacturing employment in Virginia has continued to increase while showing no growth nationally.[1] Table 6

[1] See *Virginia Economic Review,* July 1963, pp. 4–5.

TABLE 6. EMPLOYMENT IN SELECTED VIRGINIA MANUFACTURING, 1960; PERCENT-
AGE OF CHANGE, 1950–60

| Industry | Total employees (thousands) | Pct. change 1950–60 | Pct. white-collar 1960 |
|---|---|---|---|
| Textile mill | 36.4 | −10 | 10.1 |
| Food & kindred | 32.9 | 56 | 23.0 |
| Chemicals & allied | 32.5 | −5 | 25.5 |
| Electrical machinery | 8.9 | 8,800 | 46.8 |
| Primary metal | 7.0 | 112 | 31.1 |
| Machinery (except elec.) | 5.0 | 150 | 34.9 |
| Rubber and plastics | 3.3 | 313 | 21.7 |

*Sources: Va. Econ. Rev.,* July 1963, and Bureau of the Census, *Population: 1960,* text and
Appendix.

analyzes Virginia's three largest manufacturing industries and four of its
fastest-growing. Percentage figures on white-collar employment in these
growth industries, as compared with the white-collar average for all
manufacturing (22.1 percent) and all employment (40.4 percent) in
Virginia, reveal the impact these industries have had on Virginia's
occupational structure.

Service industry employs well over half of all workers in Virginia, and
over half of all workers in service industry are white-collar employees.
Table 7 examines trends in employment of white-collar workers for
selected service industries that recorded significant increases during the
fifties.

TABLE 7. TRENDS IN WHITE-COLLAR EMPLOYMENT FOR SELECTED SERVICE IN-
DUSTRIES, VIRGINIA, 1950–60

| Industry | 1960 Total employees (thousands) | 1950–60 Increase in white-collar (thousands) | 1950–60 Percent increase Total empl. | 1950–60 Percent increase White-collar |
|---|---|---|---|---|
| Public administration | 130.6 | 28.5 | 31.6 | 43.5 |
| Other prof. services | 101.8 | 34.7 | 73.4 | 71.8 |
| Medical & related | 48.8 | 11.6 | 71.9 | 61.0 |
| Finan., ins., & real est. | 47.1 | 16.2 | 56.6 | 61.8 |
| Communications | 15.4 | 3.5 | 48.3 | 49.4 |
| Business services | 12.8 | 5.2 | 174.3 | 151.0 |

*Source: Va. Econ. Rev.,* July 1963, Appendix.

The most rapidly growing white-collar occupations in Virginia are in the fields of accounting and auditing, design, engineering, the natural and social sciences, nursing, personnel and labor relations, management and administration in trade and public administration (federal and state) and in such clerical occupations as bank tellers and cashiers, medical and dental office attendants, office machine operators, payroll clerks, receptionists, secretaries, and typists. In sales occupations large increases have been recorded among demonstrators, real estate agents and brokers, stock and bond salesmen, and salesmen working for manufacturing concerns.[2]

In science and technology the growth in Virginia for most engineering occupations exceeded the national increase, but in one important field (aeronautics) it was almost negligible. State increases in the employment of natural scientists were significantly behind in the critical areas of mathematics and physics. Technicians increased more rapidly in Virginia than in the nation, except in the critical field of electricity and electronics.[3]

### Industrial Development and Education

Within the white-collar group there is a decided shift toward higher levels of formal educational training. National statistics show that the average educational achievement for professional and technical workers is now in excess of four years of college. For each of the remaining categories (managerial, clerical, and sales) average educational achievement is in excess of four years of high school.[4]

Virginia's emphasis on industrial development has brought into focus the supporting role which must be played by the educational system in providing skilled workers at all levels. Manufacturing employment in the nation has been greatly affected by sweeping technological change. Automation has eliminated many jobs, changed many others, and created many new ones. Such developments have caused a drop in production workers, offset to some extent by large increases in employment of supervisory, professional, office, and other nonproduction workers.[5] The fact that over 70 percent of the new growth in Virginia manufacturing employment between 1950 and 1960 was in white-collar jobs is a reflection of this trend. The need to keep education abreast of changing knowledge and skill requirements, for both new and old workers, will continue to grow in importance.

[2] This does not include sales engineers.

[3] See *Virginia Economic Review*, July 1963, Appendix.

[4] See U.S. Department of Labor, *A Report on Manpower Requirements, Resources, Utilization and Training* (Washington, D.C., March 1963).

[5] See U.S. Department of Labor, *op. cit.*, p. 5.

Another salient feature of industrial growth has been the narrowing time lag between fundamental scientific discoveries and their application in technology (nuclear power, transistors, and lasers, for example). It has been estimated that in a dozen of the most rapidly growing metropolitan areas in the nation essentially all the new industry in the 1950–60 decade was science-derived.[6]

This kind of growth is reflected particularly in employment trends of scientists and engineers, as well as research and development expenditures. Between 1954 and 1960 the number of scientists and engineers grew from 1.4 percent of the labor force to 1.8 percent. Expenditures for research and development are expected to reach $20 billion in 1964, double the amount expended in 1957.[7]

Table 8 shows how the employment of scientists and engineers is distributed among the various agencies which sponsor and finance research and development activities. The growth of industrial research and development since 1954 is particularly noteworthy. In that year only 27 percent of industry's engineers and scientists were engaged in research and development; in 1958 the proportion had risen to 33 percent; by 1960 the proportion was 37 percent, almost equivalent to the percentage employed in production and operation (38 percent), with the remainder employed in managerial duties (8 percent) and miscellaneous assignments (17 percent).[8]

TABLE 8. DISTRIBUTION OF SCIENTISTS AND ENGINEERS BY SECTOR, UNITED STATES, 1959

| Sector | Number | Percent |
|---|---|---|
| Government | 170,000 | 15.5 |
| Colleges and universities | 112,000 | 10.2 |
| Industry | 807,000 | 73.6 |
| Nonprofit organizations | 6,000 | 0.6 |

*Source:* U.S. Department of Commerce, *Studies in Scientific and Engineering Manpower (Part 1)* (Washington, D.C., October 1963).

Although detailed comparable statistics for Virginia research and development are not available, the general impression is that the state is lagging somewhat behind the nation. For example, Virginia's scientists and engineers constitute 1.6 percent of its labor force, as compared with

[6] See L. V. Berkner, "Whither Graduate Education," *Physics Today,* July 1963, p. 27.
[7] Data courtesy of the Division of Industrial Development (Governor's Office) and the Virginia Polytechnic Institute.
[8] See U.S. Department of Commerce, *Studies in Scientific and Engineering Manpower (Part 1)* (Washington, D.C., October 1963), pp. 6–7.

the national average of 1.8 percent, and with the 2.1 percent to 4.6 percent of the leading industrial states.[9]

In Virginia, much of the employment in research and development is concentrated in government laboratories in the northern Virginia and lower Tidewater areas, as well as in commercial research and development agencies in northern Virginia. A relatively small portion is sponsored by nonprofit agencies, colleges, and universities.

The growing importance of technicians in an industrial economy is widely recognized, but there remains much confusion in the public mind about the training and occupations of technicians. The general inclination is to identify them with traditional blue-collar craftsmen rather than with the white-collar group.

The job of the technician in industry, however, lies between that of the skilled craftsman and the engineer, utilizing both manipulative skills and technical knowledge. Technical specialties in industry apply to a number of fields, such as computing, drafting, designing, maintenance and repair, production control, quality control, technical writing, and technical sales.[10]

The versatility and superior technical knowledge of the technician are in greater demand now than formerly, primarily because of rapid changes in production procedures and in products themselves. But there is another factor behind the growing importance of technicians. This derives from recognition of the fact that much of the routine work in technological industry is being performed by graduate engineers when it could just as easily be performed by technicians with less extensive training. The use of technicians as engineering aides could free the engineer for high-level creative and developmental work.

Recognition of the utility of the technician is growing in other professional fields also, particularly in medicine and dentistry. It has significant implications for administrative and managerial occupations, where technically trained secretaries can relieve highly paid executives of much routine work.

Finally, the importance of the technician is coming into critical focus in one particular field—electronic data processing. The increasing application of computers to administrative, management, and fiscal procedures in every conceivable field of business and industry is creating a demand for computer technicians on a tremendous scale.

Employment of technicians in the over-all Virginia economy runs considerably behind national levels, even though the state increase during

[9] See National Science Foundation, *Profiles of Manpower in Science and Technology* (Washington, D.C., 1963), pp. 30–33.

[10] Dr. Lynn A. Emerson, "Technicians for Industry," a paper presented at the 43rd Annual Convention of the American Association of Junior Colleges, 1963.

the fifties exceeded national increases. The 1960 census shows a Virginia ratio of 0.37 technician for every scientist and engineer. The national ratio is 0.73 technician for every scientist and engineer. To achieve a proper balance in the employment of technicians, the Engineering Manpower Commission has recommended a minimum ratio of at least two technicians for every scientist or engineer.[11]

Higher income levels and urbanization generate demands for goods and services that are reflected in growing employment in such areas as trade and business and professional services. This, in turn, will have a continuing impact on the educational system in terms of the high proportion of white-collar employees, particularly professional ones, which service-type industry requires.

One of the service areas most sensitive to the influence of higher economic levels comprises the medical and other health professions. Virginia's position relative to national levels in health services has been steadily improving, but is still significantly below national averages.

A second professional area in which supply and demand are a critical problem for Virginia is teachers for the public schools. Above average increases in the employment of teachers were recorded in Virginia during the fifties. Relative to need, however, recent studies indicate a severe shortage of qualified teachers, particularly acute in the elementary schools. In the 1962–63 school year, for example, there was a net shortage of 893 teachers, which was relieved to some extent by employing 303 teachers on special licenses and by increasing teaching loads.[12]

In addition to these specific problems, there is evidence that the growth of the economy and the direction of development for the total society will be increasingly determined by the availability of more people with higher levels of training. In these terms the employment demands of the economy become a function of the supply of trained people at higher and higher levels of skill.

This trend reflects particularly the need to increase the supply of high-level personnel in science and technology, especially people with graduate and postgraduate training. It was observed earlier that much of the postwar industrial development in this country involved expansion of science-derived industry, springing out of the translation of basic scientific discoveries into products and procedures of applied technology. But "the creation of new industry, new products and devices, new methods and applications from the new technology arises from the

[11] From unpublished data submitted by Dr. Lynn A. Emerson to the Governor's Commission on Vocational Education, November 1963.

[12] See State Council of Higher Education, Virginia, *Teachers for the Public Schools of Virginia – Present and Future,* a report to the Governor and General Assembly of Virginia, February 1964, p. 22.

creative and imaginative insights of scientific and technological leaders who have access to the very limits of knowledge. Without that flavor of top skill for real innovation, men of lesser skills will lose their opportunity."[13]

In the new technology it is the work of graduate scientists and engineers in advancing the limits of human knowledge that actually creates the wider spread of jobs at lower levels of knowledge and skill and, in turn, stimulates economic growth for the total society. Based on statistics for the fifties, it has been estimated that for each Ph.D., the employment of from five to ten engineers at the bachelor's level can be recorded. And for each such engineer, the employment of ten to fifteen technicians and skilled craftsmen is indicated.[14]

While Virginia needs to adjust and improve its educational system in many respects and at all levels, perhaps there is no greater problem than the one of substantially augmenting total efforts in graduate training and in research and development oriented to the new technology. Such increased efforts are essential if the state is to adapt itself effectively to the most obvious direction of future industrial and economic growth.

## Virginia's Educational System

Virginia's schools, colleges, and universities are not yet fully geared to meet the new demands being placed upon them by a changing economy. Statistics on vocational programs and enrollments in secondary and postsecondary schools show that too few Virginia boys and girls are currently preparing to enter the labor force with adequate white-collar training. Data on college and graduate resources indicate that the efforts of Virginia's colleges and universities are not commensurate with the national efforts to increase the supply of high-level technical, managerial, and professional personnel and otherwise to support the advance of an industrial economy.

In view of the growing importance of technicians in manufacturing and other aspects of the state's industrial economy, the dearth of technician training must be viewed as the most significant weakness in Virginia's current educational programs below college level. The most astonishing factor, however, is the continuation of extensive programs in agriculture, basic trades, and crafts at the secondary and postsecondary levels, in spite of the large decline in employment opportunities in these fields. At the college and graduate levels a major weakness is the limited opportunity available for college training relative to the large upsurge in

[13] Berkner, *op. cit.*, pp. 27–28.     [14] *Ibid.*

population. This is reflected primarily in comparative statistics on college admissions, college enrollments, and the outmigration of college students.

Generally, high school and postsecondary programs in white-collar skills lead to employment opportunities in sales, clerical, supervisory, and technician categories. Table 9 provides projections for Virginia of new employment in these areas, based upon rates of increased employment during the fifties.

TABLE 9. ESTIMATES OF NEW WORKERS NEEDED IN SELECTED OCCUPATIONAL CATEGORIES IN VIRGINIA, 1960–70

| Detailed occupation | New workers needed by 1970* | Annual need |
|---|---|---|
| Technicians (except medical and dental) | 20,736 | 2,073 |
| Managerial | 18,190 | 1,819 |
| Clerical and kindred | 124,045 | 12,404 |
| Sales | 47,452 | 4,745 |

*Source: Vocational and Technical Education in Virginia, Present and Future Needs* (Report of the Governor's Commission on Vocational Education; Richmond, November 1963).

* Includes both expansion and replacement needs.

The major vocational training effort in Virginia is provided through the public school system, operated by local school districts with supplementary assistance from the State Department of Education. Table 10 lists the kinds of state-supported vocational services and shows enrollments (in-school and adult) for the 1962–63 school year.

TABLE 10. IN-SCHOOL AND ADULT ENROLLMENTS BY VOCATIONAL SERVICES IN VIRGINIA, 1962–63 SCHOOL YEAR

| Program | In-school | No. of schools* | Adults | No. of schools* |
|---|---|---|---|---|
| Agriculture education | 13,315 | 227 | 48,860 | 208 |
| Business education | 63,103 | 403 | 1,536 | 16 |
| Distributive education | 2,907 | 107 | 11,970 | 104 |
| Homemaking education | 62,197 | 421 | 29,233 | 188 |
| Industrial arts | 48,688 | 280 | None | None |
| Voc. Industrial education | 8,709 | 113 | 15,329 | 71 |

*Source: Vocational and Technical Education in Virginia.*

* There are over 500 high schools in the system.

Many states have developed vocational training in separate vocational high schools and postsecondary area vocational schools. In Virginia there are seven area schools (two of which operate as divisions of degree-granting colleges), with some opportunities for high-school youth but mostly serving post-high school youth and adults. Although these schools are limited largely to programs in the basic trades and skilled crafts, several have programs in business and distributive education and training for technicians. In addition, three other degree-granting colleges operate training programs for technicians as separate divisions or off-campus branches. Table 11 summarizes programs and enrollments for

TABLE 11. PROGRAMS AND ENROLLMENTS IN POSTSECONDARY INSTITUTIONS IN VIRGINIA

| Program | No. of schools | Enrollment |
|---|---|---|
| Basic trades and skilled crafts | 7 | 1,330* |
| Business education | 3 | 307† |
| Distributive education | 4 | 82† |
| Technician training | 8 | 1,600‡ |

*Source:* Unpublished data from the Governor's Commission on Vocational Education, November 1963.

\* 1962–63.        † 1961–62.        ‡ Approximate for 1962–63.

these postsecondary institutions.

In addition to the three public institutions offering postsecondary business education, approximately thirty proprietary business colleges operate in Virginia, with an estimated enrollment of approximately 3,000.[15]

The continuing emphasis in Virginia on vocational training for agriculture, home economics, and blue-collar skills is out of step with the growing demands for white collar workers. During the fifties, in fact, agricultural enrollments actually increased 38 percent, whereas agricultural employment declined 42 percent. Training-related employment of 1961 graduates of blue-collar programs averaged only 67.5 percent of those available for employment, and in several instances ranged between 11 and 34 percent of those available.[16]

Although the large in-school enrollments in business education are

[15] From unpublished data of the Governor's Commission on Vocational Education, November 1963.        [16] *Ibid.*

encouraging, the trend in clerical training is toward more postsecondary education. Accordingly, proprietary business colleges are carrying the major burden for this upgrading. Because of the expense involved, little has been done by any institution to expand training in data processing.

There are large adult enrollments in distributive education programs which are designed to prepare individuals for mid-management, supervisory, and sales positions, primarily in trade. It appears, however, that such enrollments consist mostly of persons already employed who are upgrading their skills or taking refresher courses.

Programs for technicians cover electronic, industrial, civil and highway drafting, air conditioning and refrigeration, and instrumentation technologies. Out of the total estimated enrollment in Virginia for 1962–63, 685 were employed adults. Accordingly, full-time enrollment of in-school youth training for future employment as technicians was less than 1,000.[17]

In response to these problems the 1964 Virginia General Assembly acted to create and finance a new state-operated system of postsecondary technical training centers whose curriculums are to be oriented in the direction of high-level skills, including the white-collar occupations. Additional money was provided for the public school system to adjust its vocational programs at the secondary level (including adult programs sponsored by the system). Local and state officials are currently engaged in an extensive reorganization of the programs to bring them more into line with the demands of the economy.

The number of accredited college-level institutions operating in Virginia is fairly impressive—50 in all, 22 of which are public and 28 private. Thirteen of the public institutions are degree-granting schools; the remaining 9 are two-year community colleges. There are 17 private degree-granting colleges and 11 junior colleges. (Not included in these totals are highly specialized institutions, such as seminaries, a conservatory of music, a company-operated apprentice school, and a graduate institute in textile technology.)

The programs of the private colleges are confined almost exclusively to the liberal arts, although many of these schools train substantial numbers of public school teachers; two of the private institutions operate law schools, and one has a highly successful graduate program in business administration. By and large, however, the preponderance of effort in the private college system is at the undergraduate level.

The program resources of the public college system are extensive. Offerings in the arts and sciences, engineering, business administration, medical and other health professions, law, architecture, and education

17 *Ibid.*

are provided. Four institutions offer work at the doctoral level, and four others at the master's level.

Public two-year colleges are a relatively new development in Virginia. Contrary to a national trend, these institutions operate as branches of degree-granting institutions and are limited primarily to college-transfer and preprofessional work. Their direct impact on occupational training for white-collar employment has been negligible to date.

One of the chief limitations of the public college system is the small enrollment capacities of most of the institutions, the net effect of which is to restrict severely the opportunities for specialized occupational training. The contrast between demand and opportunity is revealed in Tables 12 through 14 dealing with comparative statistics on high-school graduation, college enrollments, and degree production.

Table 12 shows that, in spite of a temporary decline in the number of Virginia youth reaching age eighteen annually, Virginia boys and girls are

TABLE 12. TRENDS IN NUMBER OF 18-YEAR-OLDS, HIGH-SCHOOL GRADUATION, AND COLLEGE ADMISSION, VIRGINIA, 1960–63

| Year | 18-yr.-olds | High-school grads. | Grads. as % of 18-yr.-olds | No. enter. college | Enter. coll. as % of h. s. grads. |
|------|-------------|--------------------|-----------------------------|--------------------|------------------------------------|
| 1960 | 64,393 | 30,262 | 47.0 | 11,708 | 38.6 |
| 1961 | 68,982 | 34,521 | 50.0 | 13,731 | 39.7 |
| 1962 | 66,131 | 33,316 | 50.4 | 13,755 | 41.2 |
| 1963 | 64,117 | 34,197 | 53.3 | 14,534* | 42.5 |
| 1964 | 72,523 | 37,577* | 51.8 | 16,459* | 43.8 |
| 1965 | 81,967 | 45,146* | 55.1 | 20,361* | 45.1 |

*Source:* Biennial report of the State Council of Higher Education, Richmond, 1964.

* Estimated

graduating from high school and seeking admission to college in steadily increasing numbers. A projection of these trends indicates that by 1970, 63.1 percent of the eighteen-year-olds will be graduating from high school, with 51.6 percent of the graduates going on to college.

Although public colleges are relatively numerous in Virginia, their enrollment capacities are atypically small: no four-year college (residential or urban) has a current undergraduate enrollment in excess of 6,000 students; lowest is 1,100, and the average is approximately 2,900. All two-year colleges are well under 1,000 in enrollment.[18]

The continuation of limited enrollment capacities in the face of a

[18] From enrollment reports of the State Council of Higher Education.

growing college-age population has acted to increase restrictions on college opportunity in Virginia, in comparison with both the region and nation. Table 13 reveals Virginia's standing in relation to the South and the nation in terms of three basic indicators of college opportunity.

Enrollment limitations relative to demand are especially critical at teacher-training institutions. For the past three years these have been

TABLE 13. COMPARATIVE STATISTICS ON COLLEGE ENROLLMENT, GRADUATE EN-
ROLLMENT, AND NET OUTMIGRATION FOR VIRGINIA, THE SOUTH, AND THE NATION

| Category | Va. | South | U.S. | Va. rank |
|---|---|---|---|---|
| 1960–61 college enrollment as a percent of college-age popula- lation (18–21) | 23.5 | 28.7 | 39.2 | 13* |
| 1963–64 graduate enrollment as a percent of total fall enrollment | 4.7 | 6.2 | 11.2 | N.A. |
| Fall 1963 net outmigration of Virginia residents going to college† | 10,200 | — | — | 4‡ |

*Sources:* Southern Regional Education Board, *Statistics for the Sixties* (Atlanta, 1963); U.S. Office of Education, *Residence and Migration of College Students* (Washington, D.C., 1963).

N.A. — not available.
* Among 16 Southern states of the Southern Regional Education Board.
† It should be noted, however, that approximately 7,500 of these outmigrants are residents of northern Virginia localities who commute to District of Columbia colleges.
‡ Among all states.

among the public institutions of Virginia that have collectively been unable each year to accommodate approximately 700 qualified applicants (mostly women) at the college of their first choice.[19] This situation is all the more critical in view of the fact that teacher training, perhaps alone among the high-level white-collar programs, is primarily oriented to providing a supply of trained personnel adequate for intrastate needs.

Table 14 provides another indication of restricted opportunity in terms of those wishing to obtain baccalaureate and graduate degrees. Since Virginia's population constitutes 2.2 percent of the total national population, it is reasonable to assume that the state is providing adequate opportunities in college and graduate training if the number of degrees conferred by Virginia institutions bears an equivalent relationship to total degrees conferred by all colleges in the country. The table shows that this is not the case, and that the gap is quite substantial at the master's and doctoral levels.

[19] From reports of the Advisory Committee on Admissions, State Council of Higher Education.

TABLE 14. EARNED DEGREES CONFERRED IN ALL FIELDS BY LEVEL, VIRGINIA AND U.S. 1961–62

|  | Va. | U.S. | Va. as a % of U.S. |
|---|---|---|---|
| 4-yr. bachelor's & 1st professional | 6,320 | 382,822 | 1.6 |
| 1st professional requiring 5 or more years | 700 | 37,663 | 1.8 |
| 2nd level (master's) | 707 | 84,889 | 0.8 |
| Doctoral | 94 | 11,622 | 0.8 |

*Source:* U.S. Office of Education.

The same approach reveals the relative weakness of Virginia's effort to provide advanced training in support of an industrial economy. Table 15 analyzes Virginia's and the nation's degree production related to employment in specific white-collar fields in science and technology. Generally, the pattern of Table 14 is repeated, with the lowest proportions appearing at the master's and doctoral levels.

A final indication of Virginia's lag in keeping its system of higher

TABLE 15. EARNED DEGREES CONFERRED IN SCIENCE AND TECHNOLOGY, BY FIELD AND LEVEL FOR VIRGINIA AND U.S., 1961–62

| Field and Level | Va. | U.S. | Va. as a % of U.S. |
|---|---|---|---|
| *Biological sciences* | | | |
| Bachelor's | 310 | 16,977 | 1.8 |
| Master's | 24 | 2,642 | 0.8 |
| Doctoral | 14 | 1,338 | 1.1 |
| *Engineering* | | | |
| Bachelor's | 667 | 33,053 | 2.0 |
| Master's | 112 | 8,909 | 1.3 |
| Doctoral | 10 | 1,207 | 0.8 |
| *Mathematics* | | | |
| Bachelor's | 250 | 14,609 | 1.7 |
| Master's | 44 | 2,680 | 1.7 |
| Doctoral | 3 | 396 | 0.7 |
| *Physical sciences* | | | |
| Bachelor's | 349 | 15,892 | 2.2 |
| Master's | 44 | 3,929 | 1.1 |
| Doctoral | 27 | 2,122 | 1.3 |

*Source:* U.S. Office of Education.

education abreast of the times comes from an analysis of research expenditures in the colleges and universities. In the fiscal year ending June 30, 1962, public institutions of higher learning expended $9.1 million on research activities—17.8 percent of the total expenditures for educational and general operations. The national average for research expenditures at all colleges, public and private, for the same year was 20 percent of total expenditures.

Furthermore, over three-fourths of these expenditures in Virginia went for medical and agricultural research, with only modest amounts allocated to basic scientific and technological fields. Table 16 shows the distribution of funds among the various fields of research.

## Summary

The statistical evidence presented in this section has highlighted the obsolescence of much of Virginia's vocational training efforts at the high-

TABLE 16. ORGANIZED RESEARCH EXPENDITURES IN PUBLIC INSTITUTIONS OF HIGHER LEARNING IN VIRGINIA, FISCAL 1961–62

| Field | Amount (thousands) | Pct. of total |
|---|---|---|
| Medical & health | $3,962 | 43.4 |
| Agriculture | 3,273 | 35.8 |
| Engineering | 876 | 9.6 |
| Physics | 247 | 2.7 |
| Chemistry | 166 | 1.8 |
| Psychology | 59 | 0.7 |
| Mathematics | 49 | 0.6 |
| Humanities | 47 | 0.5 |
| Education | 39 | 0.4 |
| Biology | 37 | 0.4 |
| Other sciences | 107 | 1.2 |
| Miscellaneous & unclassified | 269 | 2.9 |
| Total | $9,132 | 100.0 |

*Source:* Fiscal reports of the State Council of Higher Education.

school level, the dearth of specialized skill programs at the postsecondary level, the limitations on opportunity at the undergraduate level, and inadequate resources for graduate training and research, particularly those which stimulate the growth of technological industry.

General corroboration of this evidence is contained in a recent survey of Virginia business and industry conducted by the Virginia State

Chamber of Commerce.[20] Amid many favorable comments on the quality of graduates from the Virginia educational system (as well as some not so favorable), Virginia businessmen voiced their great concern at what appears to be a shortage of specialized personnel being graduated in all fields and at all levels, but particularly in advanced science and technology. Equal anxiety was manifested about the concentration of college resources in a relatively few locations, resulting in a comparative lack of opportunity in many areas for advanced training, especially for continued education and upgrading of specialized personnel already employed.

On the other hand, there are also encouraging signs that the political, educational, and business leadership of the state is making or recommending progressively greater efforts to overcome the more obvious deficiencies. As previously noted, recent legislative action has provided the means to improve secondary vocational training and expand post-secondary opportunities. There are growing sentiments for combining the expanded postsecondary skill programs with the existing two-year branch college program and thus to generate a statewide system of comprehensive community colleges, in much the same fashion that has proved so effective in a number of other states.

Public and private colleges are stepping up their efforts to provide more effective services for the growing economy, particularly in the urban areas where needs are tending to concentrate. Efforts to consolidate and improve resources for graduate training and research are emerging through activities like those of the Virginia Associated Research Center. This may very well be the forerunner of other significant developments in a cooperative and coordinated statewide approach to the problem of providing Virginia with a center of graduate education on a par with any in the country.

To what extent these efforts will be successful in solving Virginia's education problems depends basically on how far and how rapidly the state wishes to go in supplying the necessary financial support. National indices continue to show that Virginia ranks comparatively low, in spite of a steadily improving position in regard to ability.[21] To bring the state up to national averages for many of these indices will undoubtedly require a major revision of the tax structure. In any event it is certain that education—particularly college and graduate education—in Virginia cannot keep pace with the times without a substantial and rapid increase in public support, because the costs involved in overcoming the existing

[20] See Education Committee, Virginia State Chamber of Commerce, *Higher Education and the Economic Development of Virginia* (Richmond, Va., 1963).

[21] See, for example, Virginia Education Association, *Where Virginia Ranks, 1964,* (Richmond, Va., March 1964).

lag are much more than can be realistically financed from nontax sources.[22]

The conclusion is inescapable: Virginia is not developing its human resources to their full potential. If Virginia's educational system is to serve the growing economy more effectively, public policy and private attitudes must support the conviction that education is a sound investment—not a burdensome cost. A vigorous and contemporary system of education is itself a stimulus to economic growth, reflecting as it does the forward-looking interests of the people who both support it and utilize its services.

[22] Total operating expenditures for public higher education in Virginia are currently approaching $200 million a biennium, from all sources. A recent publication of the Council of State College Presidents estimates that nearly this much will have to come from tax funds alone by 1970–72 if Virginia is to reach national averages in such indices as college-age enrollments and per-student expenditures. Currently tax funds provide public college operating budgets with nearly $50 million a biennium. An estimate by the Council of Higher Education based on past trends indicates that tax expenditures for operating budgets in higher education will not reach $100 million a biennium by 1970–72.

6

# Tomorrow's Virginia
# How the Birth Patterns of the 1960's
# Shape the Population of Virginia

*Robert C. Cook, President*

*Population Reference*

*Bureau, Inc.*

A nalogies are frequently attempted between the body-biological of man and the body-social-and-political of human culture. These analogies often confuse rather than clarify—and all too frequently invite erroneous conclusion.

The body-biological is a one-shot venture. It begins as a single cell, a fertilized egg, differentiates according to the mysterious directives of the genetic code, and undergoes amazing transformations and the emergence of specialized cells constituting tissues, organs, and organ systems. The human body-biological goes through the stages of man outlined by Shakespeare—crawls, talks, walks, reproduces, moves (if the Fates have been kind) into what are now overhopefully called the "golden years," and, in the end, dies.

The body-social-and-political is a very different kettle of fish. It is an abstraction—potentially immortal. Its "cells" are people. In the United States today it is made up of over 190 million human bodies-biological, of all ages, of two sexes, of several races comprising individuals of most varied genetic potentials, all cast into a vast array of specialized roles, occupational and cultural. The human constitution of the body-social-and-political is determined in a dynamic pattern of change modulated by three components and three only: birth, death, and migration. For the world as a whole, migration obviously is not a factor.

The structure of a population with respect to age and sex is determined by the number of births and by the number and timing of deaths. Within the past century the world has seen a remarkable change in the interplay of birth and death in structuring populations because of the phenomenal success mankind has achieved in controlling mortality. Traditionally the inroads of mortality were extremely heavy, especially in the early years of life. For a population to survive, very high fertility was necessary to balance such massive mortality. Under these conditions only a fraction of the children born—hardly more than 50 percent under favorable conditions and frequently less than a quarter—survived to maturity. Life expectation at birth averaged no more than thirty years.

Today 95 percent of the babies born in the United States survive to vote and marry. This fact has resulted in the emergence of populations enjoying greatly increased life expectation, with many more older people than was the traditional pattern throughout the ages. Life expectation at birth is now about seventy years in the United States. Since the effectiveness of mortality control has been greater with respect to females than males, modern populations have an increasing proportion of women. Other features of a population modulated by current trends in fertility and mortality will be explored with respect to the state of Virginia.

Virginia stands fourteenth among the states in population. Population density is 100 per square mile, twice the United States average. By 1960 Virginia ranked nineteenth in rate of growth (with a decade increase of 19.5 percent compared with 18.5 percent for the country as a whole).[1]

During the period 1950–60 the population of Virginia grew at an average rate of 1.8 percent a year. This rate will double the population in about forty years. Virginia's rate of natural increase—annual gain of births over deaths—was 1.46 percent in 1962.[2] Since the 1960 census the population has moved up from 4 million to 4.4 million. This is a slightly slower growth than the South Atlantic states as a whole (2.0 percent a year) and faster than neighboring North Carolina (1.5 percent a year). The rate of natural increase in the United States is about 1.6 percent a year. Virginia's birth rate in 1960 of 24.1 annual births per 1,000 population declined slightly to 23.9 in 1961. Comparable rates for the United States are 23.7 in 1960 and 23.3 in 1961.[3] The birth rate varies considerably in different parts of the state. It is highest in Prince William County (36.1) and lowest in Bland County (12.0). Virginia's death rate was 8.7 in 1960, slightly below the United States rate of 9.5. The highest rate was in Accomack County (14.5) on the Eastern Shore, the lowest, Buchanan County (5.9) in the mountains.[4]

Virginia is divided into three major geographic areas: Tidewater, Piedmont, and Mountain (including the tramontane Shenandoah Valley). The mountain areas are predominantly rural and comprise thirty counties with 24 percent of the population. In the Piedmont counties are found 46 percent of the population.

The Tidewater region, comprising thirty-four counties and 30 percent of the population, contains two metropolitan areas (Newport News–Hampton and Norfolk-Portsmouth), with Richmond lying between Tidewater and Piedmont. In these three metropolitan areas are

---

[1] U.S. Bureau of the Census, *U.S. Census of Population: 1960,* Series PC(1)–1A, Tables 15, 16.

[2] The birth rate of Virginia was 23.1 and the death rate 8.5 per 1,000 population in 1962.

[3] U.S. Bureau of the Census, *Statistical Abstract of the United States: 1964,* Tables 49, 65.

[4] Based on U.S. Bureau of the Census, *County and City Data Book, 1962,* Table 2.

centered the major industrial complexes of the state. Of the 212 standard metropolitan statistical areas (SMSA's) in the United States delineated by the 1960 census, five are in Virginia and a sixth—the Washington metropolitan area, extends into Virginia and Maryland.[5] The Richmond-Norfolk area comprises the southern end of that 600-mile spreading megalopolis which extends from Portsmouth, New Hampshire, to the Virginia capes.

The structure of the population of Virginia today shows great regional differences. Here we can isolate in microcosm the various aspects of the "population problem" at the national level. In the metropolitan areas the problems of urban sprawl, deteriorating central cities, and their renewal are to be found as throughout the nation. Between 1950 and 1960 about 44 percent of the counties in Virginia lost population compared to about 50 percent for the nation as a whole. There are problems of population pressure and of population vacuums as elsewhere. Great differences are found within the state in per capita and family income, in education, and in racial composition.

The population of the Appalachian counties[6] contains a smaller proportion of Negroes than does that of most of the New England states. In some of the tideland counties Negroes constitute nearly half of the population, a proportion which approaches that of the District of Columbia (53 percent).[7] As is true elsewhere in the United States, these

[5] The 1960 census divided Virginia into standard metropolitan statistical areas (A–F) and state economic areas (1–10) as follows: *Area A*, Roanoke Co., Roanoke city; *Area B*, Arlington and Fairfax cos., Alexandria and Falls Church cities; *Area C*, Chesterfield and Henrico cos., Richmond city; *Area D*, Princess Anne and Norfolk cos., Norfolk, Portsmouth, South Norfolk, and Virginia Beach cities; *Area E*, York Co., Hampton and Newport News cities; *Area F*, Amherst and Campbell cos., Lynchburg city; *Area 1*, Buchanan, Dickenson, Lee, Tazewell, and Wise cos., Norton city; *Area 2*, Bland, Carroll, Grayson, Russell, Scott, Smyth, Washington, and Wythe cos., Bristol and Galax cities; *Area 3*, Alleghany, Bath, Botetourt, Craig, Floyd, Giles, Highland, Montgomery, Pulaski, and Rockbridge cos., Buena Vista, Clifton Forge, Covington, and Radford cities; *Area 4*, Augusta, Clarke, Frederick, Page, Rockingham, Shenandoah, and Warren cos., Harrisonburg, Staunton, Waynesboro, and Winchester cities; *Area 5*, Albemarle, Culpeper, Fauquier, Greene, Loudoun, Madison, Orange, Prince William, Rappahannock, Spotsylvania, and Stafford cos., Charlottesville and Fredericksburg cities; *Area 6*, Amelia, Appomattox, Bedford, Buckingham, Cumberland, Dinwiddie, Fluvanna, Goochland, Louisa, Nelson, Nottoway, Powhatan, and Prince Edward cos., Colonial Heights and Petersburg cities; *Area 7*, Brunswick, Charlotte, Franklin, Halifax, Henry, Lunenburg, Mecklenburg, Patrick, and Pittsylvania cos., Danville, Martinsville, and South Boston cities; *Area 8*, Caroline, Charles City, Essex, Gloucester, Hanover, James City, King and Queen, King George, King William, Lancaster, Mathews, Middlesex, New Kent, Northumberland, Richmond, and Westmoreland cos., Williamsburg city; *Area 9*, Accomack and Northampton cos.; *Area 10*, Greensville, Isle of Wight, Nansemond, Prince George, Southampton, Surry, and Sussex cos., Hopewell and Suffolk cities.

[6] Appalachian counties in Virginia are Alleghany, Bath, Bland, Botetourt, Buchanan, Carroll, Craig, Dickenson, Floyd, Giles, Grayson, Highland, Lee, Pulaski, Russell, Scott, Smyth, Tazewell, Washington, Wise, Wythe.

[7] There were fifteen counties in 1960 whose nonwhite population was over 50 percent of the total population. In the county of Charles City 83.3 percent of the population was nonwhite in 1960.

elements in population structure are not static. Viewed in the appropriate time scale of generations rather than years, Virginia is in a virtual maelstrom of population change.

In recent years migration from other states has been a minor factor in Virginia's population change in contrast to the situation in some other parts of the country. (California is currently gaining about 1,400 new residents a day through migration from other states.) For the decade of the 1950's the balance of migrants into Virginia and departures from the state showed a net gain of only 14,000. This had the effect of somewhat increasing the proportion of the white population and of reducing that of the Negroes in spite of the latter's higher fertility rate. White migration into Virginia netted an increase of 84,000. There was a net migratory loss of 70,000 Negroes.[8]

There are some anomalous aspects to population change within the state. Although the fertility of nonwhite women is considerably higher than that of white women, Virginia's white population is increasing almost twice as fast as that of the nonwhite population (which is 99 percent Negro). From 1950 to 1960 the white population grew by 21.7 percent, the nonwhite, by 11.8 percent—the higher fertility being balanced by differential migration. From 1960 to 1963 the white population is estimated to have grown by 7.4 percent, the nonwhite by less than 5 percent. The proportion of nonwhites in the population declined from

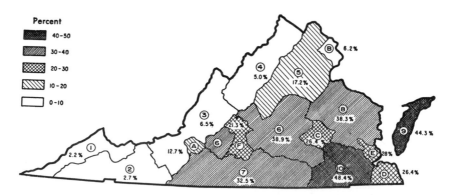

VII. *Percentage of nonwhite population, by state economic areas, Virginia, 1960. See note 5 for the counties and cities each area covers. (From U.S. Bureau of the Census, U.S. Census of Population: 1960, Series PC(3)–1A, Table 5.)*

22.2 percent in 1950 to 20.8 percent in 1960 and 20.4 percent in 1963. Distribution of the population by race is shown in Map VII. The age

8 U.S. Bureau of the Census, *Population Estimates* (Current Population Reports), Series P-25, No. 247, April 2, 1962, p. 4.

distribution of the total population and of the white and nonwhite population in 1960 is shown in Figure 1. Since 1950 the fertility of both whites and nonwhites has increased nationally. The racial and the rural-

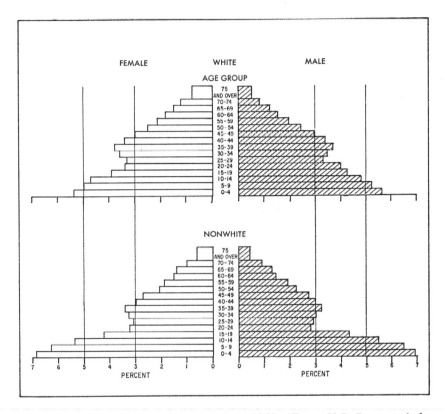

1. *Age-sex profiles, by color, Virginia, 1960. (From U.S. Bureau of the Census, U.S. Census of Population: 1960, Series PC(1)–48B, Table 16.)*

urban differences reflect, to an extent, the shorter life expectancy of nonwhites. The notable increase in nonwhite fertility presages a rapid increase in Negro population in Virginia unless the heavy out-migration continues (Table 17).

Intrastate migration has been a factor in producing large areas of declining population and in the emergence of urban areas showing very rapid population growth. The pattern of migration of population for the sixteen economic areas—six of these being standard metropolitan statistical areas—is shown in Map VIII. At the present time, as a matter of fact, Virginia has one of the fastest-growing metropolitan areas in the country. Virginia's sector of the Washington metropolitan area

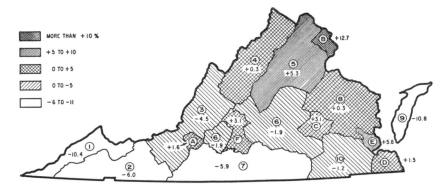

*VIII. Percentage of net migration, by state economic areas, Virginia, 1955–60. (+) denotes net in-migration; (−) denotes net out-migration. Percentages are of 1960 population 5 years old and over. (From Bureau of the Census, Population: 1960, Series PC(2)–2B, Table 31.)*

(comprising Arlington and Fairfax counties and the cities of Alexandria and Falls Church) grew by 17 percent in the years 1960–63.[9]

Another important variable in the structure of the population is residence and occupation. Along with the rest of the nation Virginia has, over the past half-century, moved rapidly from a predominantly agricul-

TABLE 17. Cumulative Fertility Ratio* by Color, and by Urban and Rural Residence, Virginia, 1960 and 1950

| Race | Total | Urban | | Percent | Rural | | Percent |
|---|---|---|---|---|---|---|---|
| | | 1960 | 1950 | Increase | 1960 | 1950 | Increase |
| All races | 2,233 | 2,024 | 1,559 | 29.8 | 2,542 | 2,437 | 4.3 |
| White | 2,096 | 1,919 | 1,503 | 27.7 | 2,358 | 2,293 | 2.8 |
| Nonwhite | 2,855 | 2,501 | 1,780 | 40.5 | 3,377 | 3,026 | 11.6 |

*Source:* U.S. Bureau of the Census, *U.S. Census of Population: 1960,* Series PC(1)–48C, Table 51.

* Children ever born per 1,000 ever married women, 15–44 years old.

tural economy to an urban industrial economy. While Virginia's urban industrial areas are growing rapidly, only 56 percent of her population was classified as urban in 1960 in comparison with 70 percent for the United States and 89 percent for New Jersey, the most highly urbanized state.[10]

The pattern of Virginia's future population is mainly being set by

[9] *Ibid.,* No. 291, p. 6.
[10] U.S. Bureau of the Census, *U.S. Census of Population: 1960,* Series PC(1)–A, Table 20.

births within the state. This is in sharp contrast to the situation in states such as Florida and California which saw a migratory increase of population of 58 percent and 30 percent, respectively, between 1950 and 1960.

The rate of natural increase—the difference between the birth rate and the death rate—is the simplest and most widely used measure of population growth. For large populations and over a short time span, it is useful. A sophisticated analysis of population trends requires taking into account the age distribution of the population and the variable fertility of women in the reproductive ages. To allow for such factors, several measures have been devised which are tied into the ratio between women in the childbearing years and the number of children per woman in this group. One of these—the cumulative fertility ratio—is based on the number of children ever born per married woman aged 15 to 44 years in a given population. This was 2.23 for Virginia in 1960 and 2.3 for the United States. It varied widely in different parts of the state.

There have been changing patterns. Fertility in the United States has changed significantly since 1910. During the depression years it declined sharply, but since the end of World War II it has approached the 1910 level.[11] Virginia's fertility has increased by 2.4 percent since 1940 for white women and by 16.2 percent for nonwhite women.[12] Until quite recently the Appalachian region experienced phenomenally high fertility. The report of the National Resources Committee published in 1938 noted that "the highest fertility in the United States is found among the women of the Southern Appalachians. . . . In Breathitt, Knott, Leslie, and Martin Counties, Ky., and in Dickenson and Buchanan Counties, Va., the population would increase 2½ times in about thirty years without emigration."[13] This represents about the maximum rate of increase possible in a relatively slow-breeding creature like man.

This situation has changed remarkably in late years. Between 1950 and 1960 the birth rates of many of the Appalachian counties of Virginia declined notably.[14] In some the declines were dramatic: 38 percent in Wythe County (from 26 to 16). In Dickenson County the birth rate declined from 32.3 in 1950 to 25.0 in 1960, a reduction of 23 percent. The rate in Buchanan County declined from 33.5 to 29.0. At first glance this would suggest that the control of fertility is making notable progress in these counties. In 1960, however, in State Economic Area 1, which includes Dickenson and Buchanan counties, the average number of

---

[11] Cumulative fertility ratios for the United States were 2,859, 1,963, 1,859, and 2,313 in 1910, 1940, 1950, and 1960, respectively. See *ibid.*, Series PC(1)-1C, Table 81.

[12] *Ibid.*, Series PC(1)–48C, Table 51.

[13] *The Problems of a Changing Population* (Washington, D.C., 1938), pp. 122–23.

[14] U.S. Bureau of the Census, *County and City Data Book, 1952*, Table 3, and *County and City Data Book, 1962*, Table 2.

children ever born per ever married woman 35 to 44 years of age was 3.9; in Area 2 it was 3.1. No other economic area in Virginia exceeded 3 for this age group. On the other hand, among women 15 to 24 years of age in 1960, the number of children ever born per married woman was 1.4 in Area 1 and 1.2 in Area 2. Comparable indices for other areas do not greatly exceed this, a fact which indicates that there may be a considerable reduction in the fertility of the younger women.

Virginia's population shows the fertility differentials characterizing the rest of the nation. Rural fertility tends to be higher than urban. The fertility of the better educated and the better circumstanced tends to be lower than the fertility of the poorly educated and the less prosperous citizens. The poverty and relatively poor education of the Negroes are major factors in this. In the Negro population the same pattern of fertility differentials is displayed as in the white population. The better-educated, well-to-do Negroes tend to have as low fertility as their Caucasian opposite numbers.

The fertility differentials within the state—regional, racial, and occupational—are the main forces modulating the future population of Virginia. The interplay between fertility and migration generates some peculiar—nay, paradoxical—situations. The nature of these can be put into perspective by considering some of the demographic and economic conditions found in the ten SEA's and six SMSA's into which the state is divided.

Map IX shows the cumulative fertility ratios of these areas. Map X is a measure of the economic conditions of these areas. Table 18 shows selected demographic characteristics in Virginia in 1960.

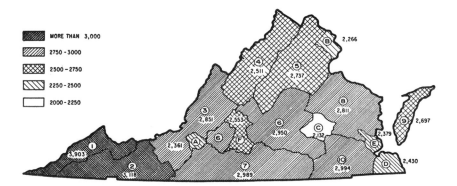

*IX. Cumulative fertility ratios, by state economic areas, Virginia, 1960. The ratios are expressed as the number of children ever born per 1,000 ever married women, aged 35–44 years. (From Bureau of the Census,* Population: 1960, *Series PC(3)-1A, Table 3.)*

TABLE 18. Selected Demographic Characteristics, by State Economic Areas, Virginia, 1960

| Area* | No. of children ever born per 1,000 ever married women aged | | | Family income median | | | Education: median years school completed | | | % urban | % non-white | Net migration 1955-60 as % of 1960 pop. 5 yrs. & up | 1960 population |
|---|---|---|---|---|---|---|---|---|---|---|---|---|---|
| | 15–24 | 25–34 | 35–44 | Urban | Rural nonfarm | Rural farm | Urban | Rural nonfarm | Rural farm | | | | |
| All areas | — | 2,322 | — | — | $4,964 | — | — | 9.9 | — | 55.6 | 20.8 | +15,000† | 3,966,949 |
| SEA 1 | 1,338 | 2,900 | 3,903 | $4213 | $3004 | $1972 | 8.9 | 7.1 | 7.2 | 13.9 | 2.2 | −10.4 | 176,125 |
| 2 | 1,203 | 2,404 | 3,118 | 4417 | 3391 | 2412 | 9.0 | 7.6 | 7.5 | 20.7 | 2.7 | −6.0 | 212,168 |
| 3 | 1,173 | 2,312 | 2,851 | 5089 | 3947 | 3198 | 10.2 | 7.9 | 7.9 | 34.2 | 6.5 | −4.5 | 184,657 |
| 4 | 1,310 | 2,291 | 2,511 | 5357 | 4178 | 3485 | 10.5 | 8.4 | 8.4 | 33.8 | 5.0 | +0.3 | 224,735 |
| 5 | 1,259 | 2,436 | 2,737 | 5324 | 4506 | 3362 | 11.0 | 9.0 | 8.5 | 25.7 | 17.2 | +5.3 | 249,767 |
| 6 | 1,404 | 2,521 | 2,950 | 4826 | 3462 | 2680 | 9.6 | 7.6 | 7.7 | 28.4 | 38.9 | −1.9 | 211,901 |
| 7 | 1,322 | 2,460 | 2,989 | 4914 | 3806 | 2375 | 8.8 | 7.7 | 7.1 | 26.2 | 32.5 | −5.9 | 319,922 |
| 8 | 1,432 | 2,667 | 2,811 | 6064 | 3861 | 3441 | 12.1 | 8.3 | 8.5 | 6.1 | 38.3 | +0.3 | 158,162 |
| 9 | 1,503 | 2,683 | 2,697 | — | 2739 | 2926 | — | 7.9 | 8.6 | — | 44.3 | −10.8 | 47,601 |
| 10 | 1,493 | 2,659 | 2,994 | 5022 | 3784 | 2287 | 9.3 | 8.1 | 7.2 | 28.5 | 48.5 | −1.2 | 161,285 |
| SMSA A | 1,146 | 2,170 | 2,361 | 5210 | 5354 | 3962 | 10.5 | 9.8 | 8.7 | 78.6 | 12.7 | +1.6 | 158,803 |
| B | 1,010 | 2,075 | 2,266 | 8433 | 7859 | 7900 | 12.7 | 11.7 | 12.4 | 90.9 | 6.2 | +12.7 | 527,098 |
| C | 1,225 | 2,135 | 2,132 | 6035 | 6239 | 5386 | 11.0 | 10.6 | 9.1 | 82.4 | 26.4 | +3.1 | 408,494 |
| D | 1,278 | 2,405 | 2,430 | 5077 | 5058 | 4504 | 10.7 | 10.0 | 8.3 | 90.2 | 26.4 | +1.5 | 578,507 |
| E | 1,226 | 2,295 | 2,379 | 5771 | 5417 | — | 11.2 | 10.9 | 10.8 | 93.0 | 28.0 | +5.8 | 224,503 |
| F | 1,208 | 2,279 | 2,553 | 5473 | 4584 | 3275 | 10.0 | 7.9 | 7.5 | 56.6 | 21.3 | +3.1 | 110,701 |

*Source:* Bureau of the Census, *Population: 1960*, Series PC(3)–1A, PC(2)–2B, and *ibid.*, *Population Estimates* (Current Population Reports), Series P-25, No. 247.

* For counties and cities comprising each economic area and each standard metropolitan statistical area, see note 5.
† For the state as a whole the total net migration, 1950–60.

Twenty-one of the mountain counties in Economic Areas 1, 2, and 3 have been designated as critical in the war on poverty.[15] The existence of such depressed areas—due in this case, in large part, to the depressed state of the soft coal market—tends to divert attention from the fact that, in the American culture as a whole, islets of poverty and deprivation are spread widely over the terrain. They are found not only in the mountains, but in and around the cities and, to a considerable extent, broadcast over the land.

Looking no closer than the sixteen areas into which Virginia is divided, we note that the median family income of the farm population in six of these is below $3,000 a year—in comparison with the highest urban area median income of $8,400 (Map X). This surely makes the point that our vaunted prosperity is spottily distributed.

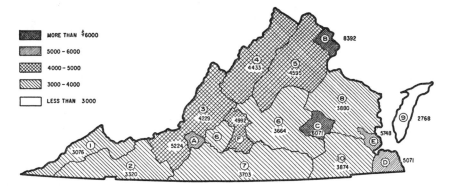

*X. Median income for families, by state economic areas, Virginia, 1960. (From Bureau of the Census, Population: 1960, Series PC(3)–1A, Table 4.)*

The demographic crystal ball can predict quite accurately what the proportion of the population in Virginia ten years old, twenty years old, or fifty years old will be in 1975. It cannot predict the proportion of the population in 1970 or 1980 which will be from one to five years old, for these additions to the body-social-and-political have not yet arrived in this vale of tears. If the present fertility trends persist, we can say that the proportion of the population which is lacking in the qualities necessary to function in the modern, increasingly complex world will be somewhat larger than it is today. The term "quality" is used here in its broadest sense. It has a definite genetic component and also important environmental and training components.

One point which must be brought into much sharper focus in connec-

[15] Two counties in Economic Areas 1, 2, 3—Montgomery and Rockbridge—are not in the Appalachia designated by the President's Appalachian Regional Commission.

tion with the battle for human rights is a clarification of the ways in which human beings are "created equal." The principle enunciated by Charlottesville's Mr. Jefferson that men are "created equal" has intriguing parallels with "equality" under the laws of nature and nature's God. Graphite, the diamond, Einstein, and the village idiot are all equal before the law of gravity. This fact cannot be adduced to justify giving your girl a ring decorated with a shining bit of anthracite or to justify lubricating bearings with diamond chips. This is so even though graphite, diamond, and anthracite are "equal" in that all are carbon and equal gravitationally. Similarly, equality before the law and before this same law of gravity cannot be stretched to expect the village idiot to elaborate the mass-energy equation. A realistic appraisal of how and in what contexts these not necessarily exclusive principles parallel each other appears to be overdue.

The question of a humane and sophisticated concern regarding the quality of tomorrow's children is of growing importance in a time of unprecedented rapid change. The nation today—as well as Virginia—finds itself in a paradoxical situation. Since 1945 several revolutionary changes have taken place in the world in which we live, and these changes affect the kind of human beings who can participate effectively in the modern world. We suddenly find ourselves in the atomic age, in the electronic age, in the age of rockets and space travel. The computer and the automated machine are revolutionizing industry, commerce, and government. The effect of these changes is to set new standards of skill and competence for those human beings who are to live in and participate in the world of tomorrow. Human muscle has virtually ceased to be salable on the labor market. The simpler mental processes are also being supplanted by increasingly complex and sophisticated machines. The Secretary of Labor recently commented that machines now operating in this new economy have built into them the equivalent of a high-school education. The young entrant into the labor force who is not adequately schooled will be at a well-nigh fatal disadvantage in finding a place for himself in the economy of tomorrow.

This can be illustrated in connection with the findings of the Task Force on Military Service established by President Kennedy on September 30, 1963. Its report, published in January 1964, found an alarming situation: that a third—possibly a half—of the young men subject to induction in the armed services were not qualified by reason of medical or mental defects. "Most of those who fail the military service aptitude tests can be expected to lack many of the qualities needed to lead self-sufficient, productive lives in the civilian economy."[16]

---

[16] The President's Task Force on Manpower Conservation, *One Third of a Nation* (Washington, D.C., 1964), p. 15.

The rejectees came mainly from backgrounds marked by deprivation and social pathology. "Almost a third of the rejectees came from families broken by divorce or separation." "Approximately seven of every 10 rejectees came from families with four or more children. . . . One out of every two rejectees comes from families with six or more children." The income of many of these families was less than $2,000—far below the poverty line. Dropouts and delinquency were major factors. The tragedy is that these youths did not choose arbitrarily to fall into such a dreary way of life. In many cases they were ensnared by inherited poverty and its quicksands of despair. Many were eager to try to repair the ravages which neglect, indifference, and inadequate schooling had wrought on them. For the nation, "by 1965, the annual 'production' of rejectees will pass the 600,000 mark and remain there."[17]

Virginia shares with the nation this grave problem, which is intimately related to the current war on poverty. Unresolved, the problem of poverty in the midst of plenty will have a devastating effect on the future destiny of the nation. It is in socially and economically submerged families, where children arrive by chance rather than by choice, that some of the nation's gravest problems are being generated. The assumption that many of these children are "wanted" has been disproved by sociological studies.

This introduces an essential aspect of the population question which at present is almost entirely ignored. In a culture of increasing complexity the question of the quality of the population in its broadest aspects assumes an ever more urgent importance. In the good—or not so good—old days, when only a minority of babies born survived to reproduce, one could assume that in man as in other organisms survival to reproduction was a test of fitness. The increasingly efficient mortality control of modern times has, in effect, democratized reproduction.

Granted a viable genotype, to be born today virtually constitutes a ticket to marriage and to the rearing of a family or, in an increasing number of instances, to fertility out of wedlock with the community acting inadequately *in loco parentis.* Somehow and in some manner means must be found whereby selective birth can take the place of selective death as an effective force to enhance the inborn quality of future generations. There is some evidence that existing birth differentials are moving in this direction, but not across the board and not very rapidly.

If the question of enhancing the quality of a population were purely a genetic exercise—were a race from Mars to dominate this planet and decide to improve the people—some "human husbandry" would be in

[17] *Ibid.,* pp. 20, 18, 29.

order. Rapid progress in developing standardized strains of humans of prescribed stature, temperament, and mental ability might be expected in a relatively few generations.

In a society of free persons—with freedom of action and decision guaranteed by law and custom—a very different situation obviously obtains. Granting the importance—even the necessity—of the maintenance of the quality of human populations, this problem represents perhaps the most difficult undertaking the human race has ever confronted. Without effective selection favoring adaptive individuals the ultimate deterioration of the gene pool of the human race is inevitable.

Free human societies being what they are—and being the only kind of societies in which the human spirit can be expected to come to full fruition birth selection has to be achieved mainly by individual volition. In a viable and biologically stable democracy responsibilities as well as privileges must be recognized and accepted.

The persuasive power of public opinion in an enlightened context can be very influential. An example of such a social force is the establishment of a pattern of late marriage in Ireland before the middle of the nineteenth century. This was effective in spite of the opposition of Church and State, and since that time this force has been a potent factor in checking Irish fertility.

Direct legal intervention will play only a minor but an important role. It may be evoked to check the reproduction of citizens whose mental capacities are so limited that they are not in position to order their own affairs. Virginia has been a pioneer in this field. In 1924 the Virginia legislature enacted a statute permitting, under medical and legal safeguards, the sterilization of feeble-minded persons. In the case of *Buck* vs. *Bell,* the constitutionality of the law was reviewed by the United States Supreme Court. The opinion upholding the statute was written by Justice Oliver Wendell Holmes. It presents a thoughtful appraisal of the difficulties of interrelating freedom and responsibility. Justice Holmes's opinion said in part:

The attack is not upon the procedure but upon the substantive law. It seems to be contended that in no circumstances could such an order be justified upon the existing grounds. The judgment finds the facts that have been recited that Carrie Buck "is the probable potential parent of socially inadequate offspring, likewise afflicted, that she may be sexually sterilized without detriment to her general health and that her welfare and that of society will be promoted by her sterilization," and thereupon makes the order. In view of the general declaration of the legislature and the specific findings of the Court obviously we cannot say as a matter of law that the grounds do not exist, and if they exist they justify the result. We have seen more than once that the public welfare may call upon the best citizens for their lives. It would be strange if we could not call upon those who already sap the strength of the state for these lesser sacrifices, often not felt to be such by those concerned, in order to prevent our being swamped with incompetence. It is better for all the world, if instead of waiting to execute degenerate offspring for crime, or to let them starve for their imbecility, society can prevent those who are manifestly unfit from continuing their kind. The principle that sustains compulsory vaccination is broad enough to cover cutting the Fallopian tubes. *Jacobson v. Massachusetts,* 197 U.S. 11. Three generations of imbeciles are enough.[18]

Recently Virginia has taken another important step in enacting a law permitting individuals who desire to do so to have themselves sterilized. This, too, is an omen of an awakening concern about fertility in its personal and social aspects in the new world which is emerging.

The tragic dilemma of the unwanted child may well be the point where the conscience of the nation focuses on the question of responsibility—not only of the individual couple but of society. One place to begin is somehow to develop a vivid public awareness of the tragedy of the unwanted child. Along with this awareness there will emerge a sense of the moral responsibility of those who undertake the joys and perplexities of parenthood. It is too late to attempt to salvage the unwanted child in the clinic and the court. The time to salvage the unwanted child is before conception. The freedom of decision to make this possible is basic to the war on poverty.

Virginia is fortunate in one respect. Its load of unemployment is below the national average. With no supercities and an economy not too highly urbanized and industrialized, it is in position to take account of these changes and to meet them with less turmoil than more congested areas of the nation.

[18] Paul Popenoe, "The Progress of Eugenic Sterilization," *Journal of Heredity,* vol. 25 (January 1934).

7

# Epidemics and Eubiotics
# The Physical Health of Virginians

*F. J. Spencer, M.B., B.S., M.P.H.*

*Chairman, Department of Preventive Medicine*

*Medical College of Virginia*

*Richmond, Virginia*

It is convenient to look at the physical health of the human population of Virginia in two phases—before and after 1912. In that year the first accurate statewide health statistics became available following the enactment of legislation requiring the registration of vital events, i.e., births, deaths, marriages, and divorces. Medically the year 1912 represents the dawn of scientific public health in Virginia. The Virginia State Department of Health, established by the General Assembly in 1908, was beginning to formulate the programs which comprise the medical care and environmental health services of today. By 1912 a decrease in communicable disease mortality was already evident, and the enthusiasm thereby engendered had not been dampened by the increase in degenerative diseases which is now occurring. Although many of the dramatic changes in therapy for individual patients were not introduced until after World War II, most methods of community disease control were known by 1912. It is the extension of these methods, aided by improved scientific techniques, which has contributed to the success of public health procedures in eliminating the infectious diseases as lethal hazards of modern society. The old attack on epidemics has been replaced by eubiotics, the science of healthy living.

## The Classical Epidemic Diseases, 1607–1912[1]

The history of health and disease in Virginia prior to 1912 is a patchwork of suppositions based upon the few reports of epidemics recorded during the seventeenth, eighteenth, and nineteenth centuries. There are no reliable data on the maladies of the indigenous inhabitants, but the severe epidemics of smallpox and other infectious diseases among them indicate that they had no natural immunity to the diseases introduced by the first settlers. The main indigenous ailments were probably those due to malnutrition; war and famine were the determining factors of population balance. The infectious diseases of England traveled across the Atlantic,

[1] See *Medicine in Virginia in the Seventeenth Century* (Richmond, 1930), *Medicine in Virginia in the Eighteenth Century* (Richmond, 1931), and *Medicine in Virginia in the Nineteenth Century* (Richmond, 1934), all by W. B. Blanton. These are the main sources of historical data before 1900.

and the earliest writings describe the "swellings, flixes, and burning fevers" which afflicted the settlers. The "flixes" and "burning fevers" were probably shigellosis (bacillary dysentery) and typhoid fever, respectively. The "swellings" may have been a result of vitamin deficiency (beriberi) or the "famine dropsy" which must have occurred during times of starvation. The association of bowel disease and sanitation may have been apparent to the settlers, because the first public health law enacted on the North American Continent at Jamestown in 1610 states:

nor shall any one aforesaid, within lesse then a quarter of one mile from the Pallizadoes, dare to doe the necesseties of nature, since by these unmanly, slothfull, and loathsome immodesties, the whole Fort may be choaked, and poisoned with ill aires, and so corrupt (as in all reason cannot but much infect the same) and this shall they take notice of, and avoide, upon paine of whipping and further punishment, as shall be thought meete, by the censure of a martiall Court.[2]

The lack of references to vector-borne disease in seventeenth-century literature is noticeable. The organisms of plague, typhus, and malaria—transmitted by flea, louse, and mosquito—do not seem to have thrived in the new colonial environment. It is reasonably certain that neither plague nor typhus was prevalent, but some doubt must be cast upon statements that malaria was uncommon in seventeenth-century Virginia. There is unquestionable evidence that malaria did occur in adjacent areas of the country,[3] and it is unlikely that Virginia escaped completely. The paucity of references to "ague" indicates that malaria, although probably present, was not the scourge in the seventeenth century that it became during the next two centuries.

During the seventeenth, eighteenth, and nineteenth centuries the classical epidemic diseases of smallpox and malaria were most prevalent, the former erupting in epidemics at frequent intervals and the latter remaining as the main endemic disease. The introduction of vaccination to America in 1801 was partly the result of the enthusiasm of Thomas Jefferson, who conducted his own experiments at Monticello. Despite this effective method of prophylaxis, smallpox continued to scourge Virginia's population until well into the twentieth century.

There is some reason to doubt the existence of yellow fever in Virginia before the end of the eighteenth century. Dr. John Mitchell's account of the epidemics of 1739 and 1741–42 probably describes another disease, possibly leptospirosis, infectious hepatitis, or relapsing fever.[4] The epidemics occurring in the last decade of the eighteenth century were

[2] Blanton, *Medicine in Va. in 17th Century*, p. 75.
[3] J. Duffy, *Epidemics in Colonial America* (Baton Rouge, La., 1953).
[4] See G. W. Jones, "Doctor John Mitchell's Yellow Fever Epidemics," *Va. Mag. Hist. Biog.*, 70 (1962), 43–48.

without doubt yellow fever, and this disease persisted during most of the next century. As yellow fever is characteristically an imported disease in temperate climates, it was natural that Norfolk should bear the brunt of the epidemics.

Cholera, the other disease imported into Virginia during the nineteenth century, was also concentrated in the Norfolk area, although epidemics occurred along the inland water and land routes. This disease became pandemic during the third decade of the nineteenth century and crossed the Atlantic in 1832. In July cases were reported in Portsmouth and Norfolk, and within two months the epidemic had penetrated inland through Richmond to central Virginia. The 1849 pandemic also arrived in Norfolk and traveled into the interior along the James and York rivers (Map XI).

The poor sanitation which contributed to the rapid spread of cholera also produced the endemic-epidemic pattern of typhoid fever which continued until recently. During the nineteenth century typhoid fever was principally a disease of the Valley of Virginia and the adjacent mountains, particularly in the Harrisonburg-Charlottesville area. As the disease was commonly water-borne, it is possible that the limestone formation of the mountains figured in the pattern of geographical distribution (Map XI).

Tuberculosis, which had been uncommon in previous years, became widely prevalent in the United States in the mid-nineteenth century. The deplorable housing and hygiene of the large number of immigrants to East Coast ports, particularly those from Ireland after the disastrous potato famine of 1845, produced an ideal environment for the tubercle bacillus. By 1900 tuberculosis had become one of three diseases responsible for a majority of the deaths in the state. The other two were smallpox and typhoid fever.

The traditional factors of population balance are three in number: famine, pestilence, and war. The preponderant importance of famine as a limiting factor of population in Virginia diminished after the seventeenth century, although malnutrition is undoubtedly still significant in the disease picture of today. Pestilence continued to wreak havoc among the people of Virginia until recently, and it remains a formidable enemy. War, however, has been responsible for an increase in mortality on only two occasions, i.e., during the War of Independence and during the Civil War. Both of these wars, particularly the latter, were fought in Virginia. As in all wars before World War II, the casualties from disease outnumbered those of battle. In the Revolutionary War the "fevers" predominated, principally typhoid it is presumed. Dysentery and scurvy were also prevalent, and, especially in the South, malaria ravaged the troops. The same diseases appeared during the Civil War, but there were

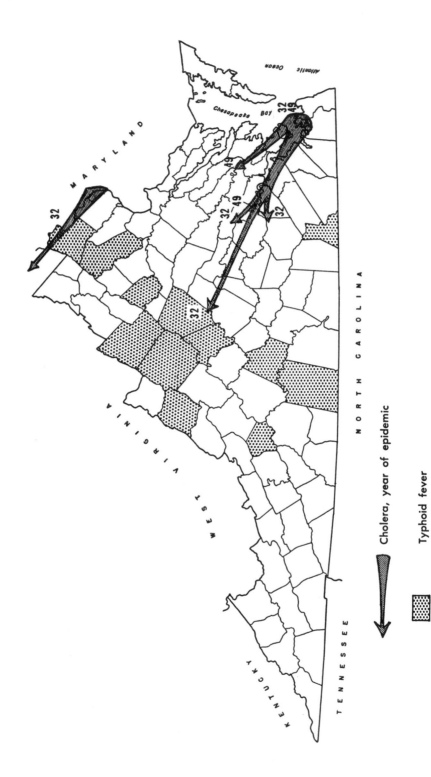

XI. *Epidemic diarrheal disease, present area of Virginia, 1830–59*

also extensive outbreaks of measles, undoubtedly caused by the concentration of nonimmune troops from rural areas. The infections carried by troops returning to their homes helped to establish the endemic diseases even more firmly on Virginia's soil.

At the turn of the century, therefore, Virginia's morbidity and mortality resulted from the classical communicable diseases of antiquity. These diseases—smallpox, typhoid, and tuberculosis—were aided and abetted by the many endemic diseases which from time to time attained epidemic proportions: dysentery, influenza, puerperal fever, pneumonia, meningitis, scarlet fever, measles, whooping cough, and the vast number of unspecified respiratory and bowel infections which contributed to the depressing picture of infant mortality.

## *The Transition to Noncommunicable Diseases, 1912–64*[5]

The scientific control of the communicable diseases in Virginia began with the expansion of public health services established in the nineteenth century. The decrease in epidemic disease is exemplified by the decline of typhoid fever. The death rate dropped from 27.3 per 100,000 in 1914 through 5.1 in 1929 to 0.07 in 1959. The case rate in 1962 was 4 per 1,000,000, and only 14 deaths from typhoid fever have occurred in Virginia during the past ten years. Pure water supplies, coupled with the introduction of modern methods of sewage disposal, were the greatest single factor producing this trend. The drop in mortality was unaffected by antibiotics, which were not available until the 1940's, and the use of typhoid vaccine played a minor role. The geographical distribution of typhoid fever was also changed by the installation of central water supplies, the rural epidemics of the nineteenth century becoming the typical urban single-source outbreaks of the present era.

The classical infectious diseases were replaced by some "new" communicable diseases, also microbial in origin, especially poliomyelitis. This disease emerged as the "infantile paralysis" of the first part of the twentieth century and was firmly entrenched in Virginia by the 1930's. Severe epidemics continued to occur at sporadic intervals until the introduction of poliomyelitis vaccine in the mid-1950's produced a dramatic decrease in morbidity. Apart from a slight increase in case rates in 1957 and 1958, the trend in poliomyelitis in Virginia has been downward since 1953 (Figure 2).

Another disease, whose virus resembles that of poliomyelitis, has been

[5] See Commissioner of Health, Commonwealth of Virginia, *Annual and Biennial Reports* (Richmond, 1909–62), which are the main sources of historical and statistical data after 1900.

epidemic in Virginia during and since the 1880's. Pleurodynia, an alarming but nonfatal disease, was first described on the North American continent in June 1888 by Dr. William C. Dabney, professor of obstetrics and the practice of medicine at the University of Virginia.[6] During the epidemic that occurred at that time a synonym now in worldwide use, "the devil's grip," was coined for the syndrome by Dr. William F. Cooper of Rappahannock County. This synonym was officially changed in Virginia to "Dabney's Grip" in 1923, when an epidemic of more than 3,000 cases was reported. In 1934 another outbreak of some 2,000 cases of "that unusual disease, Dabney's grippe

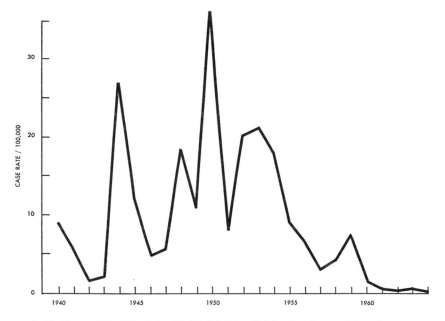

*2. Poliomyelitis, Virginia, 1940–64. The 1964 value is provisional.*

occurred in Virginia." In 1961 a smaller outbreak of pleurodynia was described in Virginia in association with a new syndrome apparently resulting from infection with the same virus.[7]

Rocky Mountain spotted fever, a complete misnomer, is endemic in Virginia. This tick-borne rickettsial disease was originally described at the end of the nineteenth century in the Rocky Mountain region and was thought to be confined to that part of the country. In 1930 a number of

[6] "Account of an Epidemic Resembling Dengue, Which Occurred in and around Charlottesville and the University of Virginia, in June, 1888," *Am. J. Med. Sc.,* 96 (1888), 488–94.

[7] W. Siegel, F. J. Spencer, D. J. Smith, J. M. Toman, W. F. Skinner, and M. B. Marx, "Two New Variants of Infection with Coxsackie Virus, Group B, Type 5, in Young Children: A Syndrome of Lymphadenopathy, Pharyngitis, and Hepatomegaly or Splenomegaly, or Both, and One of Pneumonia," *New Eng. J. Med.,* 268 (1963), 1210–16.

cases were reported in Virginia. Since that time the eastern seaboard states have been shown to be the main focus of this disease. Virginia consistently reports more cases each year than any other state, and its annual total of cases far outnumbers that of all the Rocky Mountain states. The disease in Virginia is transmitted by the dog tick and is endemic in the Piedmont area. Very few cases occur in the mountains or Tidewater Virginia. The use of antibiotics has lowered the mortality from this disease.

The hazards of the acute communicable diseases have been reduced to those of morbidity. They are no longer the determinants of mortality that they were fifty years ago. Their place has been filled by the degenerative diseases, most of which occur in the aging population which characterizes society today (Figure 3). In 1920, 7 of the 10 main causes

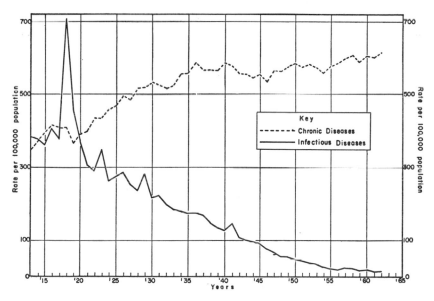

3. *Deaths due to selected infectious and chronic diseases, Virginia, since 1913.*

of death in Virginia were infections, whereas in 1962 only 1 was. The leading cause of death in 1920 was pulmonary tuberculosis. This disease was not listed among the ten main causes of death in 1962. Heart disease, not among the ten in 1920, is at present the first cause of death. Cancer, also not among the ten in 1920, was comparable to pellagra and puerperal fever as a cause of death. In 1962 cancer was the second commonest cause of death, while pellagra and puerperal fever have not appeared in the list of "important causes" of death in Virginia since the sixth revision of the World Health Organization's manual on the international classification of death came into use in 1949.

The situation facing Virginia today is like that of the rest of the country, i.e., the necessity of controlling an increasing amount of noncommunicable disease morbidity and mortality without a parallel increase in medical personnel and services. It is a platitude that all health professions and agencies must participate in the assault on disease. Certainly, even though more physicians may be graduated, the demand for increased services cannot be met by the medical profession without ancillary help. Physical health is balanced upon the two points of disease control and health promotion. In general, disease is treated within the well-established bounds of the traditional doctor-patient relationship. Consideration of the health of a group, however, introduces may factors from the physical, biological, social, economic, and cultural environment. The physical health of Virginians must therefore be viewed as affected not only by the practice of individual medicine but also by the action of the agencies responsible for the control of the total environment.

## Official and Voluntary Health Agencies

Public health in Virginia is the responsibility of the Virginia State Department of Health with the exception of some of the larger cities which have independent health departments. The structure of the State Health Department is ideal insofar as it enables a strong central administration to supervise local units. Each local health department is allowed to initiate individual programs in disease control and health promotion as long as they conform to broad state policies. The advantage of this latitude, however, is sometimes negated by a lack of uniformity in health regulations. There are still too many counties, for instance, which do not have a local ordinance requiring sanitary sewage disposal. The increase in shigellosis and salmonellosis in Virginia during the past decade (Figure 4) shows that diarrheal disease is prevalent in the rural areas where water-supply and sewage-disposal methods are more primitive than in the cities. Salmonellosis, a disease of animals and humans, is chiefly concentrated in the poultry-producing region of the Valley of Virginia, although, like shigellosis, it is endemic throughout the state.[8] That a decrease in shigellosis occurs with the installation of modern means of obtaining water has been demonstrated.[9]

Virginia, unlike many states, has complete coverage by local public

[8] F. J. Spencer, "Enteric Disease in Virginia, 1952–1960: Epidemiology and Control," *Va. M. Monthly*, 89 (1962), 413–21.

[9] A. C. Hollister, Jr., M. D. Beck, A. M. Gittelsohn, and E. C. Hemphill, "Influence of Water Availability on Shigella Prevalence in Children of Farm Labor Families," *Am. J. Pub. Hlth.*, 45 (1955), 354–62.

health services. The thirty-seven State Health Department units usually consist of a health district of 3 to 5 counties and occasionally include a small city. Each local health district is directed by a physician, often with a postgraduate degree in public health. The use of professional administrators of public health is in its infancy, and so far Virginia has not subscribed to the idea that the lay administrator can be a valuable part of the health services. The acceptance of hospital administrators by the medical profession shows that lay personnel have a definite role in modern medical care. The best use of physicians in public health would

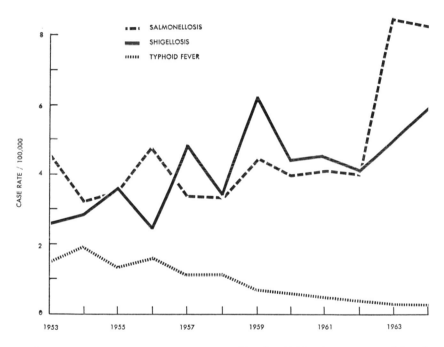

4. *Diarrheal diseases, Virginia, 1953–64. The 1964 values are provisional.*

confine their efforts to the medical aspects of community disease, where their expert knowledge is invaluable, rather than let them waste their talents wrestling with petty administrative details.

Disease control programs have usually had their inception in the individual efforts of philanthropists. The demonstrated need has then brought into being a voluntary agency, which, in turn, has stimulated official recognition and action. The number of voluntary agencies is increasing yearly as groups interested in specific disease entities promote their programs. Each of the national organizations sponsors the formation of state and local chapters. At least ten voluntary agencies have state-wide associations in Virginia,[10] and certainly many more, at present local in nature, are moving toward this goal. The national trend is toward an increasing number of voluntary agencies, and Virginia will be included in the promotion campaigns accompanying the introduction of agencies for specific disease groups as each proceeds to national recognition.

## Medical Care

Modern medical care demands the services of a team of experts, many of whom are in short supply. The usual lament—"We must have more money and more personnel"—is a convenient conscience salver. A more realistic approach is to look anew at what is available and to use it more economically and efficiently. Medical care services have developed haphazardly in Virginia, varying with the willingness of state and local governments to appropriate money for health personnel. In addition, fragmentation of total medical care services by political jurisdictions is still common in the state.

The publication of "medical topographies" in the nineteenth century culminated in Daniel Drake's classic *Principal Diseases of the Interior Valley of North America*.[11] Apart from a few local medical-topographical papers, no comprehensive work on Virginia appeared until 1939, when *Public Health in the State and Counties of Virginia* by J. F. Kendrick was published.[12] This slim volume was part of the campaign promoted by the International Health Division of the Rockefeller Foundation to increase health services by state and local health departments. Since then, no public health study of any stature has been initiated in Virginia.

The data of the United States National Health Survey point to many deficiencies in health services, particularly in the Southern states.[13] Ironically it was these states which first showed the ability of small local health departments to control diseases by improving personal and environmental health. In June 1911 the city of Greensboro, North Carolina, amalgamated with Guilford County in a county-wide full-time health program. The team of doctor, nurse, sanitarian, and clerk which

[10] Virginia State Chamber of Commerce, *Statewide Associations of Virginia* (Richmond, 1963).

[11] The full title is *A Systematic Treatise, Historical, Etiological and Practical, on the Principal Diseases of the Interior Valley of North America, as They Appear in the Caucasian, African, Indian and Esquimaux Varieties of Its Population.* It appeared in two volumes, the first in Cincinnati in 1850 and the second in Philadelphia in 1854.

[12] Richmond, 1939.

[13] U.S. Public Health Service, *United States National Health Survey* (Publications 584 and 1000; Washington, D.C., 1958–64).

developed soon became established as the basic unit of public health in rural areas. The promise of improvement of health in the South, however, has not been fulfilled because of the social, cultural, and economic factors which still plague the region.

In medical care Virginia occupies the place that is often its lot in comparative statistics of the states—i.e., among the best of the Southern states, which together constitute the lowest stratum. In 1960 Virginia spent 63 cents per capita more than did Connecticut for public health services. Despite this the age-adjusted death rate in Virginia in 1960 was almost 1 per 1,000 more than that of Connecticut. Comparative statistics for mortality in Virginia, Connecticut, and the United States during the past twenty years show that this is a continuation of a well-established trend. It is encouraging to note that the percentage of decrease in mortality in Virginia compares favorably with that of Connecticut and the country as a whole (Table 19).

TABLE 19. PER CAPITA PAYMENT FOR PUBLIC HEALTH SERVICES AND AGE-ADJUSTED DEATH RATES

| | | Age-adjusted death rates | | | | | |
|---|---|---|---|---|---|---|---|
| | | | | | Percent decrease | | |
| | Per capita payment for public health services 1959 | 1960 | 1950 | 1940 | 1940 to 1960 | 1950 to 1960 | 1940 to 1950 |
| United States | — | 7.6 | 8.4 | 10.8 | 29.6 | 9.5 | 22.2 |
| Connecticut | $2.38 | 7.2 | 7.7 | 10.0 | 28.0 | 6.5 | 23.0 |
| Virginia | $3.01 | 8.1 | 9.2 | 12.3 | 34.1 | 12.0 | 25.2 |

*Source:* U.S. Public Health Service, *Medical Care Utilization and Financing* (Publication No. 947; Washington, D.C., 1962); U.S. Public Health Service, *Vital Statistics of the United States, 1960* (Washington, D.C., 1963).

Although it was stated in 1921 that "the reduction of typhoid deaths is the accepted standard of efficiency of public health administration," some public health physicians were beginning to think of the infant mortality rate as an even more sensitive indicator of medical care. The United States Children's Bureau, formed in 1912, was encouraging states to initiate maternal and child health programs. It was soon realized that reduction of the infant mortality rate was proportional not only to infant services but also to care during pregnancy. The idea of complete prenatal care by an obstetrician was introduced.

The acceptance of the "man-midwife" is comparatively new in society. The closely kept secret of their forceps enabled the doctors Chamberlen to assert their superiority as accoucheurs in the sixteenth century, but that "great horse-godmother of a he-midwife"—William Smellie (1697–1763)—was the man who finally toppled the midwife off her perch as chief birth attendant.[14] The midwife was a familiar figure in Virginia fifty years ago and in fact is still active today in many rural areas. The 5,000 midwives in Virginia delivered 30 percent of the 66,-000 babies born during 1923. The State Department of Health, sensibly realizing that at birth often "the only available help is an untrained midwife," initiated a midwife-licensing program. The training of midwives has been an integral part of this program since its inception. The State Health Department today "issues and renews permits as well as retirement certificates to midwives and assists in their supervision." The number of midwives in the state dropped below 1,000 ten years ago and in 1963 only 497 midwives were registered in Virginia.

The term "midwife" has the unfortunate connotation of the old-time "granny" in the United States. But there is a vast difference between these Sairey Gamps and the modern nurse-midwife, who is educated as a nurse and trained or experienced in public health. The latter

brings to the field of maternal and child health a particular breadth of experience and understanding of the technical, medical, social, and emotional problems of the childbearing period.

In addition to giving maternity nursing services, the nurse-midwife has responsibility, with medical supervision, for the education, health, and obstetrical management of selected pregnant women and for the early recognition of deviations from the normal in the health of the mother and of the new born baby.[15]

The pioneer work in nurse-midwifery in Virginia's neighboring state Kentucky in 1925 has blossomed into courses in seven institutions in this country. There are fewer than 1,000 of these trained nurse-midwives in the United States. The nurse-midwife is the nucleus of obstetrical services in most countries outside North America. The infant mortality rates in the technically developed countries in which midwives practice are, in many instances, lower than those in the United States. Virginia ranks fifth in total expenditure on maternal and child health programs in the country and spends more than double the amounts allocated by most of the Southern states for these services (Table 20). The infant mortality rate in Virginia is, however, appreciably lower than that of only one or two neighboring states. The infant mortality rate in Virginia

[14] H. Graham, *Eternal Eve: The Mysteries of Birth and the Customs That Surround It* (London, 1960).

[15] American College of Nurse-Midwifery, *Education for Nurse-Midwifery* (Santa Fe, N.M., 1958).

compares unfavorably with that of the United States and even more so
with those of other countries (Table 21). There is less variation in
maternal mortality rates, but the merit of comparing statistics based on
the small numbers of deaths associated directly with pregnancy is
questionable. Even so, it is estimated that half of the deaths contributing

TABLE 20. EXPENDITURES FOR MATERNAL AND CHILD HEALTH, 1960

|  | Population (male 0–14; female 0-44) | Total expenditure | Per capita expenditure |
|---|---|---|---|
| United States | 94,047,181 | $78,634,877 | $ .84 |
| Pennsylvania | 5,601,597 | $ 8,362,188 | $1.49 |
| Virginia | 2,104,544 | $ 4,148,989 | $1.97 |
| Florida | 2,438,704 | $ 2,884,857 | $1.18 |
| North Carolina | 2,487,534 | $ 1,793,640 | $ .72 |

*Source:* Public Health Service, *Medical Care Utilization and Financing.*

TABLE 21. INFANT MORTALITY RATES AND REDUCTION OF INFANT MORTALITY, 1950, 1962

| Countries | 1962 Rank* | 1962 Rate | 1950 Rank* | 1950 Rate | Percent decrease since 1950 |
|---|---|---|---|---|---|
| Netherlands | 1 | 15.3 | 3 | 25.2 | 39.3 |
| Sweden | 2 | 15.3 | 1 | 21.0 | 27.2 |
| Norway (1960) | 3 | (1960) 18.9 | 5 | 28.2 | 33.0 |
| Finland | 4 | 19.2 | 11 | 43.2 | 55.9 |
| Australia (1961) | 5 | (1961) 19.5 | 2 | 24.5 | 20.4 |
| Denmark | 6 | 20.1 | 7 | 30.7 | 34.5 |
| New Zealand | 7 | 20.3 | 4 | 27.6 | 26.5 |
| Switzerland (1961) | 8 | (1961) 21.0 | 8 | 31.2 | 32.7 |
| United Kingdom | 9 | 22.1 | 9 | 31.4 | 29.6 |
| Ireland | 10 | 24.2 | 13 | 46.2 | 47.6 |
| U.S. total | 11 | 25.3 | 6 | 29.2 | 13.4 |
| white |  | 22.3 |  | 26.8 | 16.8 |
| nonwhite |  | 41.8 |  | 44.5 | 6.1 |
| Va. total | — | 29.2 |  | 34.6 | 15.6 |
| white |  | 23.7 |  | 28.5 | 17.1 |
| nonwhite |  | 46.5 |  | 51.5 | 9.7 |

*Source:* Modified from U.S. Public Health Service, *Second National Conference on Health Training* (Publication No. 1087; Washington, D.C., 1963).

* Ranked according to 1962 or latest figures.

to maternal mortality are preventable. All measurements of mortality are lower for the white than the nonwhite population.

Infant care in Virginia is met by private medicine or, for indigent patients, in health department well-baby clinics. Most children receive a physical examination before entering school. School health services vary from complete supervision by full-time school physicians and nurses to an occasional visit to the school by a public health nurse. A confusing element in school health services is that some are administered locally by the health department and some by the department of education.

The need for improved health services during childhood and adolescence is demonstrated by the health status of selective service registrants (Table 22). In 1962 more than half the registrants from Virginia were

TABLE 22. STATUS OF SELECTIVE SERVICE REGISTRANTS EXAMINED, 1961 (PERCENTAGE DISTRIBUTION)

| | Found accept- able | Total disquali- fied | Medically disquali- fied only | Failed mental test only | Failed mental test and medically disquali- fied | Adminis- tratively disquali- fied |
|---|---|---|---|---|---|---|
| United States | 51.3 | 48.7 | 23.5 | 19.9 | 2.6 | 2.7 |
| Iowa | 67.1 | 32.9 | 26.7 | 3.4 | 1.5 | 1.3 |
| Kansas | 69.7 | 30.3 | 25.0 | 4.2 | 0.9 | 0.2 |
| South Carolina | 33.8 | 66.2 | 14.3 | 46.7 | 5.0 | 0.2 |
| Virginia | 47.4 | 52.6 | 19.2 | 25.3 | 4.7 | 3.4 |

*Source:* U.S. Bureau of the Census, *Statistical Abstract of the United States* (Washington, D.C., 1963).

disqualified, although the percentage medically unfit was less than that of the United States. The percentage deferred for failing both mental and physical examinations was more than the United States figure, and this was also true for those who were failed on the mental test only. Although many of the reasons for rejection indicate minor disabilities, the inference is that many Virginians enter adulthood at a physical disadvantage.

The pattern of aging in Virginia reflects that of the United States. The increased population over 65 years of age needs more medical care than does that at any other age, except perhaps for the first few days after birth. The care of the newborn infant, however, generally requires the employment of only one or two skilled individuals, i.e., a doctor and a nurse, and is concentrated within a hospital. Care of the aged not only uses the skills of the doctor and nurse but also all the ancillary workers in medicine and the social services. The recognized undesirability of institutional care for older people points to the necessity for home care programs. There are few of these in the state of Virginia (Map XII).

The annual influx of migrant laborers is a seasonal threat to the health of the inhabitants of the Commonwealth. It is estimated that 12,500 migrant workers enter Virginia each year as part of the "Atlantic Coast

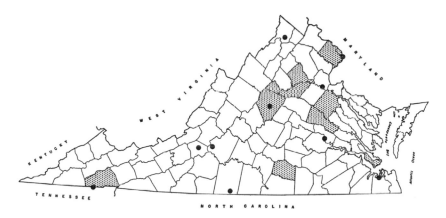

*XII. Visiting nurse services, Virginia, 1964*

Movement."[16] Most of the laborers come from their winter homes in Florida or other Southern states. The season begins in May with the strawberry crop on the Eastern Shore and continues with the picking of potatoes, tomatoes, and beans until November. Another group of migrant laborers picks peaches and apples in the Roanoke–Northern Valley area from August through November. One of the migrants coming from Pennsylvania in 1959 introduced typhoid fever to the Northern Valley region, and an epidemic of 16 cases with 1 death resulted.[17] Apart from their menace to health, migrant laborers place a severe strain on private and public medical care facilities and finances in the areas where they work.

*Hospitals, Nursing Homes, and Medical Manpower*

The location of hospitals and nursing homes in Virginia follows the current trend toward urbanization. As the building of nursing homes to

---

[16] U.S. Senate, *The Migrant Farm Worker in America* (Report of the Subcommittee on Migratory Labor of the Committee on Labor and Public Welfare; Washington, D.C., 1960).

[17] U.S. Senate, *Public Health Programs for Improving Migratory Health Services* (Report No. 699, Testimony of Senator Harrison A. Williams; Washington, D.C., 1961).

serve the aging population is a new phenomenon, they are somewhat more urban in distribution than the hospitals. There are 117 hospitals in Virginia, excluding federal and state institutions other than the two medical school hospitals (Table 23). The total of 14,029 beds is equivalent to 3.5 beds per 1,000 population compared to 4.5 for the

TABLE 23. HOSPITALS, VIRGINIA, 1964

|  | Number | Beds | | Beds per 1,000 pop.* |
|  |  | Total | Median | |
|---|---|---|---|---|
| All hospitals † | 117 | 14,029 | 80 | 3.5 |
| Nonprofit | 81 | 12,046 | 100 | — |
| Proprietary | 36 | 1,983 | 40 | — |

*Source:* Virginia State Department of Health, *Virginia Hospitals* (Richmond, 1964).

\* The 1961 ratio for the United States was 4.5.
† Excluding state hospitals other than medical schools.

United States. The median bed capacity of nonprofit institutions is almost three times that of proprietary hospitals, two-thirds of which are located in the mountains west of Roanoke. This distribution results from the necessity of establishing small hospitals close to the populations they served in the first three decades of this century. The advantages of regional hospitalization were not recognized until comparatively recently.

Virginia has 159 nursing homes with 5,156 beds, a ratio of 18 beds per 1,000 persons aged 65 or more (Table 24). The national average is 22.1. Twenty-five (16 percent) of the institutions in Virginia are in Richmond. There are 15 nursing homes for Negroes in the state with

TABLE 24. NURSING HOMES, BY COLOR, VIRGINIA, 1964

|  | Number | Beds | | Ratio per 1,000 aged 65 or over* |
|  |  | Total | Median | |
|---|---|---|---|---|
| All nursing homes | 159 | 5,156 | 24 | 17.8 |
| White | 144 | 4,930 | 24 | 21.0 |
| Nonwhite | 15 | 226 | 14 | 4.1 |

*Source:* Virginia State Department of Health, *Convalescent and Nursing Homes of State of Virginia* (Richmond, 1964).

\* The 1961 ratio for the United States was 22.1.

226 beds or 4 beds per 1,000 persons 65 or over. Most of the nursing homes have been built or converted during the past ten years and are proprietary institutions. The inherent undesirability of profit institutions which brought about the increase in nonprofit hospitals in Virginia is manifest in many of the homes. In 1960 there were 307,267 nursing home beds in the United States. Forty-seven percent of these beds were unacceptable because of fire or health hazards.[18] No estimate could be made of unsatisfactory conditions of nursing or medical practices. Although the Virginia State Department of Health licenses nursing homes, there are intrinsic difficulties in the program. The main element of discord is that there is no answer to the question: "What happens to the patients if this nursing home is closed? Where can they be housed?" The location of nursing homes in Virginia does not correspond to the population distribution. Washington County, including the city of Bristol, has 7 nursing homes with 208 beds for a population of 55,455. The seven counties which are adjacent to Washington County have a total population of 195,426 and no nursing homes.

The distribution of members of the health professions in Virginia also follows the pattern of urbanization. In 1962 Virginia had an over-all ratio of 119 physicians per 100,000 population, 19 below the United States figure.[19] This low ratio of doctors per population parallels that of dentists, pharmacists, nurses, physical therapists, and the many other members of the modern medical care team. The ratio for pharmacists, for instance, was 46 in Virginia compared to 66 for the United States.[20]

The metropolitan areas of northern Virginia, Norfolk, and Richmond are well supplied with doctors. Generally the rural areas of the state have a lower doctor-patient ratio than the cities. There is, however, a distinct pattern of distribution in rural areas which indicates that there are factors which attract physicians to some locations and not to others. The previously noted doctor-patient ratio of 119 per 100,000 in Virginia's counties ranges from 503 per 100,000 in Albemarle County to 0 in King and Queen County, with a median of 66, about half the ratio for the United States. Many of the counties which exceed the median are concentrated in the urban regions already noted and also in the smaller cities of Petersburg, Lynchburg, and Roanoke. There is also a line of rural counties extending down the Valley of Virginia and on to Bristol

[18] U.S. Senate, *The Condition of American Nursing Homes* (A Study by the Subcommittee on Problems of the Aged and Aging of the Committee on Labor and Public Welfare; Washington, D.C., 1960).

[19] Commonwealth of Virginia, *Physicians for Virginia: Part I, A Study of Virginia's Medical Schools* (Richmond, 1964).

[20] P. Q. Peterson and M. Y. Pennell, *Health Manpower Source Book: Section 15, Pharmacists* (Washington, D.C., 1963).

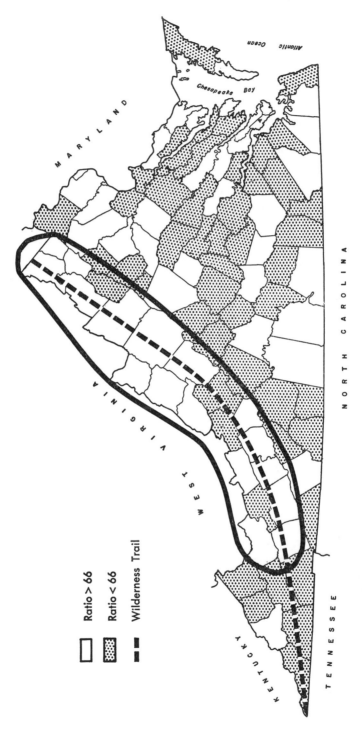

XIII. *Physician-population ratio, Virginia, 1960. The map shows the counties falling below and above the median county ratio of 66 physicians per 100,000 population.*

Ratio > 66

Ratio < 66

Wilderness Trail

which has a doctor-patient ratio of 66 or more (Map XIII). These counties cluster along the settlers' trail which led from Pennsylvania to Cumberland Gap and on into Kentucky, i.e., the Wilderness Trail. The natural development of small towns and cities along this trail produced a series of trade centers supplying the population of the mountains which enclose the Valley. These centers were the natural places for doctors to settle and establish practice. Today most of the small cities or towns have a local hospital in which the physician can practice hospital medicine. The capacities of these hospitals range from some 30 to 250 beds. The proximity of medical centers in Charlottesville, Roanoke, and Bristol, Tennessee, renders these locations even more attractive to physicians.

## Environmental Health

Public health departments are branches of government and therefore labor under the disadvantages of being restricted by administrative boundaries. The political divisions of the state of Virginia, bounded arbitrarily by natural barriers and human design, cannot keep diseases without their jurisdictions any more than Hong Kong could prevent the exodus of Asian influenza from Red China in 1957. It is difficult to change the boundaries of political districts, but this fact should not prevent the formation of health districts based upon demographic patterns. The fragmentation of medical services in metropolitan areas between cities and their surrounding counties is still too common. Admittedly some progress has been made in extending the cheapest environmental services, e.g., water supply, to suburban areas, but very often this precedes the extension of the more expensive sewage disposal system by several years. The unlimited use of water places a heavy load upon the suburban septic tank, and in many areas this becomes evident as a pool of raw sewage in the back yard. This may contribute to the already noted resurgence of diarrheal disease. The haphazard development of suburbia is still almost uncontrolled, apart from the zoning ordinances which have been enacted in several cities and counties.

Perhaps even more repugnant to the suburban dweller is the complete lack of official garbage disposal service in most communities. The sight of an unsanitary open truck spewing garbage onto the street as it wends its unsteady way from house to house is too often encountered. This sporadic and unorganized collection of garbage is complemented by allowing it to be dumped, and not covered, in rural areas, very few of which have been specifically designated for that purpose. The resulting rats and flies increase the possibility of disease transmission.

Provision and control of four essentials are necessary for the maintenance of the health of the public—air, water, food, and shelter. The first two are heavily polluted in industrial countries. Water pollution is being dealt with satisfactorily in Virginia by the State Water Control Board, which requires that all waters of Virginia's watersheds be free from pollution. Some of the work of this government agency is, however, rendered useless by the open sewer of the Potomac, fed in areas beyond the jurisdiction of the state. Regional control obviously is necessary to complete the work already begun in Virginia. Air pollution is increasingly being implicated as a causal factor in lung disease. Practically no control measures have been attempted in Virginia beyond a few local ordinances, usually ineffective.

The two other public health necessities—food and shelter—are receiving varying amounts of attention. Adequate control of food-borne disease is accomplished by federal, state, and local legislation through health and agriculture departments. Although the clinical syndromes of scurvy and pellagra are no longer seen, minor manifestations of malnutrition are still widely prevalent in the lower socioeconomic groups. The housing authorities of the larger cities, particularly Norfolk and Alexandria, have effected some improvements in a few areas, but most of the smaller cities have no legislation even pending which would set minimum housing standards. An exception is the successful campaign in Fredericksburg, which has resulted in the elimination of one health hazard—the frost-proof toilet—and has also produced ordinances pertaining to housing and garbage disposal.[21]

On the whole, the development of coordinated government services in environmental health has been slow and confined to the larger urban areas. Without the expansion of services made possible by a unity of city and county, or state and state, it is unlikely that more than small local improvements can be made in controlling environmental menaces. Water and air do not remain within city, county, or state limits.

There is a lack of occupational health services in the United States. The ideal ratio of 1 doctor to each 2,000 employees cannot be realized with only 1,660 full-time American physicians practicing occupational medicine. Only 23 of these are in Virginia.[22] It is estimated that each employee in the United States averages 12 days a year off from work because of injury or illness. The percentage of employed civilians away from work on any one day has not changed appreciably during the past decade. The Virginia State Department of Health offers services to industry through the Bureau of Industrial Hygiene.

[21] R. O. Olmsted, "Elimination of Frost-proof Toilets and Hydrants," *Public Health Reports,* 79 (1964), 603–9.

[22] W. H. Stewart and M. Y. Pennell, *Health Manpower Source Book, Section 10: Physicians, Age, Type of Practice, and Location* (Washington, D.C., 1960).

*Summary*

The present physical health of Virginians is characteristic of a population in a modern urban environment. Infectious diseases have been replaced by degenerative diseases. There are increased demands for new types of personal and communal health services. The distribution of medical care facilities in the state corresponds to the pattern of urbanization. There is a wide variation in mortality and in medical services between the white and nonwhite populations. Statistical comparisons with other states and countries show that improvement of health at all ages is possible. Virginia's health patterns and services need to be defined, using modern statistical and epidemiological techniques. The usefulness of this type of study has been demonstrated.[23] Intelligent use of such a survey would contribute immeasurably to improving the physical health of Virginia's population.

[23] Department of Public Health, State of California, *Health in California* (Berkeley, Calif., 1957), and *Health Care for California* (Berkeley, Calif., 1960).

8

# Mental Health in Virginia

*Richard W. Garnett, Jr., M.D.*

*Professor of Neurology and Psychiatry*

*University of Virginia School of Medicine*

In general we know more about illness than we do about health, whether mental or physical. Virtually all our data are recorded in terms of illness—and officially recognized illness at that. Only by inference do we assume that what is not illness must be health. Illness and health are not distinct as black and white; rather they are represented by more or less arbitrary zones of dark and light shading into a wide intermediate area of gray. This accounts for the paradox that when we set out to talk about mental health we end by devoting considerable time to mental illness.

We are, of course, interested in more than just the mentally ill who are or have been in state and private hospitals. We would like to be able objectively to appraise, evaluate, quantify, and qualify the mental health of the whole population not just in terms of the presence or absence of identifiable illness—in psychoses, psychoneuroses, personality disorders, psychophysiologic disorders, and retardation—but also in terms of effective living, functioning, and coping with problems and in the even more subjective areas of happiness, satisfaction, creativeness, and capacity for working and enjoying life. Recent studies and reports of the Joint Commission on Mental Illness and Health[1] represent virtually the only comprehensive attempt to deal with these and other significant variables; some of the conclusions of the Joint Commission will be referred to later. Other pertinent epidemiological studies, based on intensive, community-wide analysis, have been conducted in New Haven,[2] Manhattan,[3] and Stirling County, Nova Scotia.[4] No studies deal specifically with

[1] M. Jahoda, *Current Concepts of Positive Mental Health* (1958); R. Fein, *Economics of Mental Illness* (1958); G. W. Albee, *Mental Health Manpower Trends* (1959); G. Gurin, J. Veroff, and S. Field, *Americans View Their Mental Health* (1960), R. Robinson, O. F. DeMarche, and M. K. Wagle, *Community Resources in Mental Health* (1960); and R. J. Plunkett and J. E. Gordon, *Epidemiology and Mental Illness* — Monographs 1–6, respectively, of the Joint Commission on Mental Illness and Health, published in New York by Basic Books.

[2] A. B. Hollingshead and F. C. Redlich, *Social Class and Mental Illness* (New York, 1958).

[3] L. Srole, T. S. Langner, S. T. Michael, M. K. Opler, and T. A. C. Rennie, *Mental Health in the Metropolis: The Midtown Manhattan Study* (New York, 1962) and T. S. Langner and S. T. Michael, *Life Stress and Mental Health* (New York, 1963) — vols. I and II of the Thomas A. C. Rennie Series in Social Psychiatry.

[4] A. H. Leighton, *My Name Is Legion* (1959); C. C. Hughes, M. Tremblay, R. Rapoport, and A. H. Leighton, *People of Cove and Woodlot* (1960); and D. C. Leighton, J. S. Harding, D. B. Macklin, A. M. Macmillan, and A. H. Leighton, *The Character of Danger* (1964) — vols. I–III, respectively, of the Stirling County Study of Psychiatric Disorder and Sociocultural Environment, published in New York by Basic Books.

Virginia, although many of the findings in other areas pertain to this state in a general way.

## Definitions of Mental Health and Illness

The noted psychiatrist Karl Menninger has defined mental health as the "adjustment of human beings to the world and to each other with a maximum of effectiveness and happiness." It is not, he says, "just efficiency, or just contentment, or the grace of obeying the rules of the game cheerfully. It is all these together. It is the ability to maintain an even temper, an alert intelligence, socially considerate behavior, and a happy disposition." This, he declares, is the sign of a "healthy mind."[5]

Thomas S. Langner and S. T. Michael use the term "mental disorder" as "roughly equivalent to the full range of disturbances which a psychiatrist treats." It includes the "neuroses and character disorders as well as the psychoses. It also includes a panoply of milder 'subclinical' disturbances some of which are unlikely to receive treatment." Mental illness and mental disease, on the other hand, "suggest only the most severe impairment and often imply some identifiable lesion caused by a specific agent."[6]

In a message to Congress in February 1963 President Kennedy stated that mental illness and mental retardation were "among our most critical health problems." And he went on, "They occur more frequently, affect more people, require more prolonged treatment, cause more suffering by the families of the afflicted, waste more of our human resources, and constitute more financial drain upon both the public treasury and the personal finances of the individual families than any other single condition."[7]

In this paper we will show how President Kennedy's statement applies to the United States and to Virginia in particular. In the course of the discussion it will become abundantly clear that the inclusion of this topic in a symposium on human resources is both timely and appropriate.

## Historical Review and Development of Facilities

Virginia's efforts to cope with mental illness among its inhabitants began in the colonial period. It has the distinction of having established the

[5] *The Human Mind* (New York, 1946), p. 2.      [6] Langner and Michael, *op. cit.*, p. 1.
[7] *Message from the President of the United States Relative to Mental Illness and Mental Retardation* (House of Representatives, Document 88; Washington, D.C., 1963), pp. 1–2.

first government-supported hospital in North America exclusively for the mentally ill; this was opened in 1773 at Williamsburg. The governor of the colony, Francis Fauquier, first urged the establishment of such an institution in 1766, and the House of Burgesses passed a resolution favoring the erection of a hospital for "the reception of persons who are so unhappy as to be deprived of their reason." Action was delayed, however, and in 1767 Governor Fauquier again brought up the "case of poor lunatics, a measure which I was in hope humanity would have dictated to every man, as soon as he was made acquainted with the call for it." He pointed out that against his conscience he had been forced to authorize the confinement of lunatics in the Williamsburg jail. In 1769 the House of Burgesses passed an act "to make provision for the support and maintenance of idiots, lunatics, and other persons of unsound mind." The act went on to say that "several persons of insane and disordered minds have been frequently found wandering in different parts of this Colony, and no set provision . . . [has] been yet made toward effecting a cure of those whose cases have not become quite desperate, nor for the restraining others who may be dangerous to society."[8]

The first visiting physician of the hospital was Dr. John DeSequeryra, a leading doctor of Virginia. James Galt was appointed the first keeper, and the Galt family was to be connected with the institution for nearly a century. The most eminent member of this family was Dr. John Minson Galt, who became the first medical superintendent in 1841. He and Dr. Francis Stribling, the first medical superintendent of the Western Lunatic Asylum established in 1825 at Staunton, were founding members of the Association of Medical Superintendents of American Institutes for the Insane (1844). That organization has evolved into the present American Psychiatric Association, the oldest national organization of medical specialists in the United States.

The founding of these two hospitals in Virginia coincided with the great era in the care of the mentally ill known as "moral treatment." This movement was a reflection of the philosophical and political climate of the time, as represented by John Locke, Rousseau, and Jefferson. In the medical field this movement was advocated by the great reformers of treatment of the mentally ill—Philippe Pinel and Jean Étienne Esquirol in France, William and Samuel Tuke and Henry Maudsley in Great Britain, and Benjamin Rush and Dorothea Dix in America. Rush, a contemporary and friend of Thomas Jefferson, is known as the Father of American Psychiatry. In 1847 Dr. Amariah Brigham listed the essentials of "moral treatment" as follows: "The removal of the insane from home and former associations, with respectful and kind treatment under all circumstances, and in most cases manual labor, attendance on religious

[8] Quoted in A. Deutsch, *The Mentally Ill in America* (New York, 1952), pp. 69–70.

worship on Sundays, the establishment of regular habits of self control, diversion of the mind from morbid trains of thought, are generally considered as essential in the moral treatment of the insane."[9] In many respects modern treatment of the mentally ill has turned back to "moral treatment" for its inspiration and techniques, with its renewed emphasis on rehabilitation, recreation, occupation, respect for the individual, and expectation of cure or at least of return to the community.

For the seventeenth and most of the eighteenth century few documented records concerning mental illness are extant other than occasional references to lunatics and idiots who, as indicated above, apparently wandered about the colonies. There are, however, accounts of such practices as "passing on" and "auctioning," supremely practical methods of dealing with problem cases of the day. "Passing on" occurred when a community simply transported a public charge to another community and dumped him there; this was probably only slightly more civilized than driving such a person into the wilderness. "Auctioning" was literally that; persons who were public charges were put up at auction to the highest bidder, who might then force them to work for their support. Some of the mentally ill boarded in private homes at public expense, and, of course, many of the serious cases were undoubtedly held in prisons.[10]

Other public hospitals were established in Virginia as follows: Central State Hospital, which was exclusively for Negroes, opened in Petersburg in 1865; Southwestern State Hospital at Marion in 1887; and the Lynchburg Training School and Hospital for epileptics and the feeble-minded in 1911. The De Jarnette State Sanatorium originally established in 1928 as a special "pay" unit of Western State Hospital, was designated a separate institution in 1934 as a state-supported hospital for paying patients. The Petersburg Training School and Hospital for the care of retarded Negro children was founded in 1958. The Virginia Treatment Center for Children in Richmond was completed in 1961; it is a unique institution, the only one of its kind in the country built and operated by a state. Now in the planning stage is a hospital to serve the northern Virginia area. This will be in keeping with the modern trend toward small hospitals for intensive treatment over relatively short periods.

Four private psychiatric hospitals and sanitariums—three of which were established about the beginning of the century—have played a significant role in the state in providing care for the mentally ill who are able to pay. These institutions also served as a center for early private practice on an outpatient basis. The two state-supported medical schools

---

[9] Quoted in J. S. Bockover, "Moral Treatment in American Psychiatry," *Journal of Nervous and Mental Disease*, 124 (August 1956), 1–113.

[10] See Deutsch, *op. cit.*, pp. 24–54.

with their associated hospitals and outpatient clinics established Department of Psychiatry about 1930. These have expanded rapidly and have had considerable effect in the state through better training of medical students in diagnosis and treatment of the mentally ill, through training of specialists in their residency programs, and through their influence on the medical profession and the public at large. Their programs have included short-term training courses for general practitioners and other physicians in modern psychiatric concepts and treatment. In recent years five community hospitals have established psychiatric units; this is a trend that will undoubtedly continue in the immediate future. The past ten years have seen a rapid increase in the private practice of psychiatry, but many areas remain without either private or public services and few private facilities are available to Negroes. (See Map XIV.)

In 1942 the General Assembly of Virginia created the Department of Mental Hygiene and Hospitals under the supervision and management of the State Hospital Board. The Commissioner of Mental Hygiene and Hospitals with his staff serves as the over-all administrator and coordinator of state hospitals and mental health services. At the same time a system of community mental health clinics was established. There are now twenty-five such clinics in the state, usually staffed by a full-time or part-time psychiatrist, a psychologist, and a social worker. Virginia ranks eighteenth in the nation in providing clinic services, although coverage is still far from adequate. There are three Veterans Administration hospital facilities in the state: a large primarily psychiatric hospital at Salem, McGuire's Veterans Hospital at Richmond with a psychiatric unit, and a veterans' domiciliary at Kecoughtan, which is primarily for older patients.

Although Virginia has much of which to be proud in its provision of facilities for the care of the mentally ill, the picture has a dark side. The era of "moral treatment," with its idealism, optimism, and dedication, came to an end in the 1860's. Paradoxically, this was about the time that science in general and medicine in particular were making rapid advances. With the discovery of specific causes for many illnesses, it was assumed that specific pathology—brain lesions, pathogenic organisms, or the like—would eventually be found as the etiologic agents in mental illnesses. Hence there was a loss of interest in general methods of treatment, and mental hospitals regressed into the doldrums of custodial care, with primary emphasis on security and the provision of minimal physical needs and protection. Psychiatry tended to drop out of the main stream of medicine, and the hospitals became more and more large, isolated, self-contained institutions to which ever-increasing numbers of patients were sent, always by legal commitment and with very little hope of return. Even the location of mental hospitals and their architectural

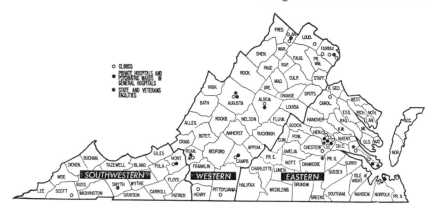

*XIV. Distribution of mental health facilities, Virginia*

design seemed based on the principle "out of sight, out of mind." As far as public mental hospitals were concerned—and they took care of 98 percent of all hospitalized mentally ill—this situation prevailed until recently.

### New Developments in Scientific Psychiatry

Despite the fact that the last quarter of the nineteenth century and the first half of the twentieth saw little progress—actually there was considerable retrogression in the care of the hospitalized mentally ill—certain major developments occurred in the general field of psychiatry. These derived principally from the epoch-making studies of Sigmund Freud and his contemporaries and successors. The development of psychoanalysis and individual psychotherapy has had a tremendous impact on Western culture. Treatment has, however, been restricted largely to the psychoneuroses, character disorders, and the problems of interpersonal relationships. Because these techniques are time-consuming and to a considerable extent experimental, they have also been expensive and therefore limited to the relatively few and the comparatively affluent. Very few of the advances of dynamic psychiatry or psychology filtered through to the state hospital population or were applied in any significant way to the treatment of the psychoses.

Between 1937 and 1940 insulin coma and convulsive therapy induced by chemical or electrical means were introduced as treatments for the major mental illnesses—schizophrenia, depression, and mania. The effect of these new treatments on the otherwise apathetic atmosphere of the mental hospitals was striking. New hope, renewed effort, and quickened interest were awakened on the part of scientific medicine. Here were physical methods, which, while not well understood, at least replaced inertia and produced rapid and tangible effects. Somewhat later came a brief period of enthusiasm for surgical methods of treatment. The initial enthusiasm for all of these forms of somatic therapy, including the even more recent drug therapies, has waned somewhat, owing to the realization that they rarely offer real cures and that the effects are often temporary, unsatisfactory, and accompanied by various undesirable side effects.

The Second World War helped to focus attention on mental health for several reasons. One was the shocking rejection rates of volunteers and draftees because of mental and emotional defects. Another was the tremendous number of servicemen discharged for mental breakdowns and various nervous disabilities, either incurred in or uncovered by duty in the armed forces. The public, the government, and the medical profession were forced to recognize the problem and the necessity of doing something about it. Doctors serving in the armed forces were confronted with many patients suffering from serious mental and physical reactions to stress. They saw the development of techniques of treatment which seemed to make sense and to be effective in a considerable percentage of cases. These were essentially the modern methods of intensive psychiatric treatment for acute disorders and the development of techniques for rehabilitation. Many doctors returned from the war desiring more training in psychiatry. Psychosomatic medicine became popular, respectable, and rewarding; psychiatry, psychiatrists, and psychiatric patients came back into the main stream of medicine. References to psychoanalysis and psychoanalysts were common in the press and on radio and stage.

The year 1935 saw the founding of the Neuropsychiatric Society of Virginia, consisting principally of the staff physicians of the public and private mental hospitals. This organization has become a district branch of the American Psychiatric Association, with over 100 members, and by its influence helps to keep Virginia abreast of national trends in mental health developments.

In 1962 the General Assembly of Virginia passed a resolution proposing that a commission be appointed to study and make recommendations for revision of the laws relating to the mentally ill. Governor Albertis S. Harrison appointed the commission, and its report was presented to the legislature at the regular session of January 1964. Virtually all of the recommended amendments were passed, considerably modernizing the statutes of Virginia and removing many archaic practices and concepts.

The Assembly recognized the need for a study in the general field of mental retardation also and in 1962 requested that a Virginia Advisory Legislative Commission study the services provided for retarded persons. The findings of this study were also submitted to the 1964 legislature.

Virginia, along with various other states, has participated in the program authorized by Congress and supported by the Department of Health, Education and Welfare to set up a special study commission to report on mental health conditions and the facilities available and needed in the state. A State Mental Health Commission consisting of about seventy prominent citizens was appointed to study conditions in Virginia and make recommendations to the governor. A public information program was to be initiated in an attempt to reach Virginians of all classes in order to ascertain what mental health programs and facilities were desired and would be supported.


*Nature and Magnitude of the Mental Health Problem*

Clifford T. Morgan estimates that one in ten Americans have some form of mental illness or serious maladjustment.[11] A survey done in Baltimore, Maryland, by the Commission on Chronic Illness concluded that 10 percent of the population were in need of psychological services.[12] The total number seeking some sort of psychological help is estimated to be about 3,000,000 a year. If these estimates are correct, there are about 17,000,000 Americans who need help but do not get it. Of those seeking help, 42 percent go to clergymen, 29 percent to general physicians, 11 percent to social agencies, and 18 percent to a psychiatrist or psychologist. One million patients are hospitalized each year for mental disorders. Five hundred thousand visit psychiatric outpatient clinics. We think that many of the 1,500,000 children under eighteen years of age apprehended by the police every year (600,000 of whom appear in court) may be mentally ill or seriously maladjusted. There are 213,000 people whose behavior is sufficiently deviant to necessitate their being kept in state or federal prisons. Between 20,000 and 25,000 people are known to commit suicide each year. (See Table 25.)

Psychiatric disorders occur more frequently and disabling symptoms tend to persist longer in families with low incomes, limited education, and poor surroundings. Although the need is greatest in this group, the demand for specific psychological services is greater in higher income groups. Members of the lower income groups are apt to be directed to

---

[11] *Introduction to Psychology* (New York, 1961), p. 161.
[12] *Chronic Illness in the United States*, vol. IV, *Chronic Illness in a Large City: The Baltimore Study* (Cambridge, Mass., 1957), p. 95.

caretaking agencies or to express their mental instability in crime, delinquency, or other forms of social maladjustment.[13] Professional personnel and facilities are in short supply, and the distribution is very uneven. Services are frequently unavailable. Experience has shown repeatedly that as facilities are made available or improved, the demand for them goes up proportionately. In 1880 the rate was 63.7 per 100,000 population in public mental hospitals in the United States. In 1944 it was 366.7—five times as high. Because improved treatment has shortened the length of hospital confinement, the number of patients in the hospital at a given time has declined since 1954 (in 1959 it was 319 per 100,000) but the admission rate continues to climb.

TABLE 25. SOCIAL PROBLEMS RELATED TO MENTAL ILLNESS OR PSYCHOLOGICAL DISORDER, UNITED STATES

| | |
|---|---:|
| Serious crimes yearly | 1,750,000 |
| Americans with criminal records | 7,000,000 |
| Children age 7–17 before juvenile courts annually | 265,000 |
| (1.2 % of that age group) | |
| Estimated annual incidence of delinquency | 2,500,000 |
| Estimated number of children in need of | |
| psychiatric help | 3,000,000 |
| Divorce rate | 1 in 4 |
| Divorce and separation rate | 1 in 3 |
| Estimated number of narcotic addicts | 50,000 |
| Estimated number of alcoholics | 3,800,000 |
| Estimated number of suicides yearly | 25,000 |

*Source:* U.S. Public Health Service, *Facts on Mental Health and Mental Illness* (Publication 543; Washington, D.C., 1962).

Does this mean that mental illness is increasing at the rate indicated by the difference between the figures of 1880 and 1944? There are reasons for doubting that the real rate has increased very much if at all.[14] One is that there is wide variation between states and regions in statistics based on admissions to public mental hospitals. The lowest figure is 116 mental hospital residents per 100,000 population in New Mexico; this compares with 589 per 100,000 in New York State and 866 per 100,000 in the District of Columbia. Probable explanations for the apparent increase are (1) the broadened concepts of mental illness or insanity, (2) readier recognition and diagnosis of mental illness, (3) more frequent hospitalization, (4) more hospitals, (5) reduction of the fear and stigma leading to greater acceptance of hospitalization, (6) prolongation of the life of hospitalized patients, and (7) longer life spans in

[13] Hollingshead and Redlich, *op. cit.*, pp. 114–35.
[14] H. Goldhamer and A. Marshall, *Psychosis and Civilization* (Glencoe, Ill., 1953).

general, leading to greater numbers developing the mental illnesses of senescence.

The mentally ill occupy over half of the total number of hospital beds — 704,769 patients out of the 1,363,217 average daily population of public and private hospitals in 1959. The average daily resident population in public mental hospitals in 1960 was 539,184. The number of admissions (including new and repeat admissions) annually to all types of mental hospitals is 550,000. More patients occupy hospital beds for mental illness than for all other diseases combined (see Figure 5).

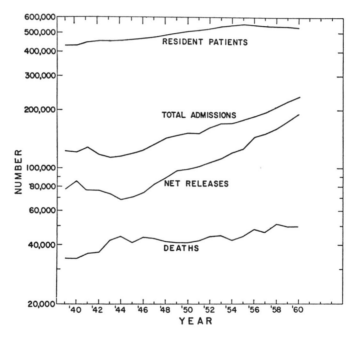

5. *Number of resident patients, total admissions, net releases, and deaths in public mental hospitals, United States, 1939–60. (From U.S. Department of Health, Education and Welfare, National Institute of Mental Health,* Mental Health Statistics, Current Reports, *January 1961.)*

It is estimated that one in twenty will spend some time in a mental hospital during his lifetime. Of every 100 school children, four will become chronically mentally ill, eight will have some type of nervous or emotional breakdown, and one will become a delinquent.

Statistics show that one out of every three registrants aged eighteen is rejected by the United States armed services. One-half of these rejections are due to mental and emotional defects and illiteracy. The highest rates of rejection occur in the Southeast and the lowest in the western plains and mountains. Thirty-one percent of the rejectees come from broken families, 9 percent have court records, 80 percent were school dropouts, and 21 percent come from families receiving public assistance.[15]

There are, of course, many medical problems related to mental and emotional ones. Most internists, pediatricians, and general practitioners estimate that approximately 50 percent of their visits are for problems that are basically of a psychological or emotional nature. A high proportion of absenteeism and unemployment in industry is due to these same factors. Many other social problems are more or less related, such as vandalism, traffic accidents, poor performance in school and school dropouts, marital discord, and extremes of fanaticism and prejudice, of aggression and passivity.

### Genetic Factors

Since the discovery of the laws of inheritance, it has been widely assumed that mental illness is largely due to heredity. This idea has been generally accepted in folklore and has contributed to the sense of stigma and shame and to the secrecy associated with mental illness. With the rise of psychodynamic theories following Freud's work and the conditioned reflex discoveries of Ivan Pavlov and, particularly in recent years, with the advances in the knowledge and influence of the social sciences, cultural or environmental theories of the causation of mental illness have been in ascendancy and genetic theories have been investigated rigorously. The true picture has finally begun to emerge. Influenced largely by the studies of Franz J. Kallman, a leading exponent of genetic studies, most authorities have become convinced that certain of the psychoses, notably "true schizophrenia" and "true manic-depressive psychosis," have a strong genetic component. Such a component probably plays an even larger part in epilepsy and mental retardation.

In the case of schizophrenia—the outstanding problem in the field of mental health and, according to many, in the entire field of public health and medicine—strong evidence has been presented that genetics is a significant factor. Kallman states: "Schizophrenia occurs in every segment of the population regardless of social or economic status. Variation in prevalence is limited in the absence of inbreeding."[16] His figures, based on extensive research and widely accepted as authentic, are given in Table 26. Recent research indicates that the genetic defect is in the

---

[15] Deutsch, *op. cit.*, p. 464.
[16] "The Genetics of Mental Illness," in *American Handbook of Psychiatry*, ed. S. Arieti (New York, 1959), I, 175–96.

*Virginia's Human Resources*

TABLE 26. EXPECTANCY OF SCHIZOPHRENIA, UNITED STATES

|  | Percent |
|---|---|
| In the general population | 1 |
| In full sibling of a schizophrenic | 14.3 |
| In half sibling of a schizophrenic | 15.1 |
| In children of two schizophrenic parents | 68.1 |
| In children of one schizophrenic parent | 16.0 |
| In diazygotic twin of a schizophrenic | 14.7 |
| In monozygotic twin of a schizophrenic | 85.8 |

*Source:* F. J. Kallman, "The Genetics of Mental Illness," in *American Handbook of Psychiatry*, ed. S. Arieti (New York, 1959), I, 175–96.

metabolic process; possibly a latent facility of the body activated by stress to bring about an abnormal change in the body chemistry. It is generally considered, however, that schizophrenia is not a single disease but a syndrome with many possible causes and types.

## Environmental Factors

The general opinion now is that a person inherits only a predisposition or tendency, which may be small or great and which requires the addition of environmental stress, inversely great or small, in order to precipitate the actual symptoms of a mental disorder, whether schizophrenia or other mental illness. Environmental stress, particularly in the early formative years and during certain critical periods such as adolescence, prolonged separation from home or familiar persons and surroundings, and child-bearing are some of the factors that may bring on an illness in the absence of any discernible genetic predisposition.

A. B. Hollingshead and F. C. Redlich in their monumental study *Social Class and Mental Illness* show that mental illness, particularly in its severer forms, is much more prevalent in low economic and social classes than in others.[17] R. E. L. Faris and H. W. Dunham have demonstrated its disproportionate distribution in various ecological areas, the highest rates of schizophrenia occurring in "deteriorated" sections of cities.[18] Obviously some of these trends are accounted for by the natural drift of the sick and handicapped into the poorer areas and into low socioeconomic classes, but plausible hypotheses have also been advanced concerning high psychopathological "breeding rates" in such areas. Con-

[17] Pp. 114–35.
[18] Quoted in R. E. L. Faris, *Social Disorganization* (New York, 1948), p. 229.

gruent findings have been made in large-scale epidemiological studies such as those of Stirling County, Nova Scotia, and midtown Manhattan referred to earlier. Aside from the relevance of environment to the causation of the major forms of mental illness, its predominant role in minor mental and other disorders is apparent, i.e., in neuroses, personality disorders, alcoholism, drug addiction, delinquency, criminality, perversions, psychosomatic illness, and marital problems and others.

Not only is environment an important factor in causation as shown in the strong correlation between incidence and prevalence, on the one hand, and, on the other, social class, economic status, and many other variables, such as age, sex, marital status, religious background, and ethnic identity; but these factors also enter into the question of whether treatment is available, whether a person is able to get treatment, and what kind of treatment he receives. Hollingshead and Redlich demonstrated this, dividing the population of New Haven into five social classes from the highest to the lowest. Table 27 shows the distribution of patients

TABLE 27. SOCIAL CLASS AND MENTAL ILLNESS

| Social class | Psychotherapy | | Organic therapy | | No therapy | |
|---|---|---|---|---|---|---|
| | No. | Percent | No. | Percent | No. | Percent |
| I | 14 | 73.7 | 2 | 10.5 | 3 | 15.8 |
| II | 107 | 81.7 | 15 | 11.4 | 9 | 6.9 |
| III | 136 | 52.7 | 74 | 28.7 | 48 | 18.6 |
| IV | 237 | 31.1 | 288 | 37.1 | 242 | 31.8 |
| V | 115 | 16.1 | 234 | 32.7 | 367 | 51.2 |

*Source:* A. B. Hollingshead and F. C. Redlich, *Social Class and Mental Illness* (New York, 1958).

getting one of the two major types of therapy or no therapy. Psychotherapy, which includes psychoanalysis, is generally considered more desirable than organic therapy, particularly for neuroses and other nonpsychotic conditions. It is also much more expensive and time-consuming. Organic therapy includes particularly electroshock and drugs.

Most authorities, even those with a strong genetic or "organic" bias, agree that environmental factors producing stress, anxiety, and frustration are a frequent if not a necessary ingredient to mental illness.

Margaret Mead, the noted anthropologist, in the Introduction to *Cultural Patterns and Technical Change* states: "While it is still not possible to say that a given culture is less conducive to mental health than another, because of our lack of cross-cultural criteria for mental disorders, it is possible to say that under situations of stress and strain, of rapid change and consequent disorientation, there is likely to be an increase in manifest mental ill health."[19] Richard L. Jenkins in his book *Breaking Patterns of Defeat* says: "A social or a cultural situation which gives rise to insoluble problems and much frustration may be expected to result in a higher incidence of schizophrenia than a social or cultural situation which gives rise to less frustration."[20]

What can we say specifically regarding the relation of these environmental, social, economic, and ethnic considerations to Virginia? Although we may tend to think of Virginians in terms of some stereotype, we know that we are far from homogeneous and, in fact, encompass a broad spectrum. Historically we have been predominantly rural and agricultural. The past fifty years have seen a marked shift toward an urban and industrial society. Particularly during and since the Second World War have we become a much more mobile and less provincial people. Traditionally we have been and still are extremely conservative — politically, socially, and economically. Nowhere has there been greater resistance to change in social customs or a more determined championing of traditional values, concepts, and habits of thinking, feeling, and living. This has given us relative stability and security, but in the face of inexorable forces of change called "progress" it has also given rise, in some, to deep feelings of frustration, anger, and bitterness and, in others, to perplexity, confusion, and anxiety.

The most significant social shift has been the rise of a new Negro in our midst and attending social changes that have been revolutionary in character. "Integration" has become the most highly charged word in our vocabulary. Regardless of the pros and cons, this concept has challenged the most basic assumptions and habits of thinking of virtually every citizen, white and colored. Fear, anger, resentment, frustration, anxiety, and guilt have been rampant among us, and our social structure as well as individual stability has been subjected to one of the severest tests of the past hundred years.

Much has been said since the Supreme Court decision of 1954 about the argument that segregation inherently damaged the personalities, gave rise to inferiority feelings, created resentment, mitigated against the sense of dignity and integrity, reduced pride and motivation to achievement, and otherwise traumatized the Negro. In some circles this decision has been decried on the ground that it was based on the "psychological and sociological theories" of Gunnar Myrdal, a Swedish sociologist, in his book *The American Dilemma*.[21] Less has been said and few admit or recognize the effect of segregation, discrimination, and exploitation on

---

[19] In *Cultural Patterns and Technical Change*, ed. by her (New York, 1955), pp. 11–12.
[20] Philadelphia, 1954, p. 218.        [21] New York, 1944.

the minds and morals of the dominant group—the corrosive effects of guilt, contradiction, anxiety, contempt, fear, and hate.

Still other aspects of the problem are becoming apparent. Drastic changes in the environment, in customs, in basic patterns, habits, goals, and expectations, also lead to anxiety and consequently to various defensive attitudes and behavior. The Negro child thrust suddenly into an all-white school experiences severe psychic trauma. He is made more acutely aware of his differences. He senses directly and indirectly the hostility, contempt, ridicule, and fear of the majority group, and he is deprived of the support of his peers and familiar surroundings. He is often unable to communicate with those around him, and there may develop a widening gap of misunderstanding, suspicion, and antagonism. Since the advent of integration many whites have been shocked to realize the existence or the depth of their prejudices, with consequent increased feelings of guilt, hostility, rationalization, and confusion and the adoption of more actively defensive attitudes and behavior.

To a considerable extent these are problems of a transitional nature such as tend to accompany any social revolution. They are also the problems associated with any minority-majority group relationships. It would, however, be a mistake to fail to recognize these as among the most serious and significant problems affecting the current mental health, or at least the "peace of mind," of Virginians. For the most part we seem to be resolving them and can take some satisfaction that the excesses and social convulsions that have occurred elsewhere have not occurred here. Margaret Mead has noted that the test of the maturity, stability, and competency of a society is its ability to develop techniques for reducing anxiety and therefore to enable people to face crises without gross disorganization.

In 1960 a group of psychiatrists had this to say regarding the effects of desegregation, which partially restates the above arguments:

During any individual's lifetime, he is frequently faced with highly complicated problems which appear to him to be insoluble. At such times he may feel helpless, torn by indecision; he may not know how to solve or even approach his problem. These dilemmas provoke feelings of uneasiness that may reach proportions of extreme anxiety. In order to cope with this anxiety, he may resort to the prevailing myths to provide a seemingly rational solution to his problem. Although such myths are without objective validity, they are maintained and transmitted in the culture as a powerful influence by virtue of the fact that they have their deep roots in individual childhood experience. To illustrate: in the United States white people have had to reconcile their belief in equality and Christian principles with their actual inhuman treatment of Negroes. In trying to solve this dilemma they have created and defended the various myths about the stereotyped Negro described above. Having created such myths, it becomes easier to justify their conduct, for principles of equality need not apply to so unworthy and inferior a group. Furthermore, through a vicious circle these myths are nourished, sustained, and perpetuated by actual present-day social and economic deprivations of Negroes.

The damaging consequences of racial myths are misconstrued as evidence to support them. American Negroes as a group are in fact multiply handicapped: socially, politically, educationally, and economically. But these handicaps are a consequence of racial discrimination rather than of racial inferiority.

The myth may serve another purpose. Individuals of any race will, from time to time, experience acute doubts about their own worth, their sexual adequacy, their acceptability. These fears and misgivings do not seem quite so intense if one focuses one's attention upon the deficiencies of others. The individual who is filled with self-contempt because of his lack of efficiency and progress on his job may turn his contempt onto the members of a racial minority, represented in myths as being stupid, lazy, irresponsible, etc. He then obtains some consolation from the thought that at least he is better than they are. But such methods of dealing with one's problems fail to reach a realistic solution of the original difficulty. Furthermore, they result in increased guilt and anxiety.[22]

In 1957 Dr. David C. Wilson, then professor of psychiatry at the University of Virginia, in a paper entitled "The Effect of Culture Change on the Negro Race in Virginia as Indicated by a Study of State Hospital Admissions," used statistics compiled by E. M. Lantz to show that there is a much higher ratio of Negro patients per 100,000 population than of white patients. Wilson also pointed out the greater incidence of mental illness in Negroes proportionately to whites since 1914. He concluded: "It is felt that the fact that there is more mental illness among the Negroes of Virginia than among the whites and more mental illness among the Negroes in 1954 than in 1914 is due in large degree to segregation and to the uncertainties of the Negro race as they cross from one culture to another."[23] Table 28 indicates that the number of Negro hospital patients per 100,000 population is approximately double that for white in 1954, and that the 1954 rate among Negroes was over twice that of 1914. Among the factors causing the differential in rates between the races and over the years, as shown in Table 29, are the availability of private facilities to the whites, the increased availability of state hospital accommodations to Negroes in 1954 as compared with 1914, and economic and other social factors leading Negroes to accept or resort to hospitalization more readily in recent years.

A striking increase is noted in Table 30 for schizophrenia in the Negro group and for cerebro-arteriosclerosis and senility in both groups.

---

[22] *Group for the Advancement of Psychiatry, Emotional Aspects of School Desegregation* (New York, 1960), IV, 37a.

[23] *American Journal of Psychiatry,* 114 (July 1957), 25–32.

TABLE 28. Number of Patients in Hospitals for the Mentally Ill, Mentally Deficient, and Epileptic in Virginia by Race, July 1, 1914 to June 30, 1954

| | White | | Negro | |
|---|---|---|---|---|
| | Total in hospital | Rate per 100,000 | Total in hospital | Rate per 100,000 |
| Average 1914–19 | 3,120 | 201.4 | 1,769 | 257.0 |
| Average 1940–45 | 7,118 | 353.5 | 4,069 | 613.8 |
| Number June 30, 1954 | 8,561 | 314.6 | 4,681 | 600.6 |

*Source:* D. C. Wilson and E. M. Lantz, "The effect of Culture Change on the Negro Race in Virginia, as Indicated by a Study of State Hospital Admissions," *American Journal of Psychiatry,* 114 (July 1957), 25–32.

TABLE 29. First Admissions after Deducting Patients Admitted because of Alcoholism, Mental Deficiency, and Epilepsy without Psychosis, by Race 1918–55

| | White | | Negro | |
|---|---|---|---|---|
| | First admissions | Rate per 100,000 | First admissions | Rate per 100,000 |
| 1918–25 | 737 | 45.5 | 411 | 59.4 |
| 1926–35 | 952 | 53.8 | 474 | 72.7 |
| 1936–45 | 1,038 | 51.5 | 626 | 94.5 |
| 1946–55 | 962 | 37.2 | 676 | 90.1 |

*Source:* Same as Table 28.

Many factors apparently contribute to the incidence of suicide (see Table 31). It is generally higher in white, Protestant, Anglo-Saxon, middle-class, urban people over the age of fifty than in others and ranks about tenth in causes of death. It is, however, the Number Two cause of death among college students, being second only to highway accidents.

*Current Status and Trends of Mental Health Care*

The history, development, and distribution of mental health facilities in Virginia have already been reviewed. How are we performing now, and

TABLE 30. RATE OF HOSPITAL ADMISSIONS PER 100,000, BY RACE AND DIAG-
NOSTIC CATEGORIES

| | White | | | | | Negro | | | | |
|---|---|---|---|---|---|---|---|---|---|---|
| Year | Cerebro-arterio-sclerosis and senility | Schizophrenia | Manic de-pressive | Syphilis | Alcoholism | Cerebro-arterio-sclerosis and senility | Schizophrenia | Manic depressive | Syphilis | Alcoholism |
| 1920 | 6.1 | 6.4 | 10.3 | 1.4 | 1.1 | 9.5 | 12.0 | 16.5 | 2.4 | 0.4 |
| 1930 | 9.1 | 9.4 | 18.9 | 1.9 | 8.1 | 19.6 | 16.1 | 9.4 | 7.8 | 0.6 |
| 1940 | 15.6 | 9.0 | 5.8 | 3.2 | 22.1 | 20.8 | 10.4 | 25.2 | 14.6 | 2.4 |
| 1950 | 15.0 | 6.4 | 2.1 | 0.9 | 12.0 | 25.2 | 14.2 | 14.0 | 13.1 | 5.6 |
| 1955 | 16.1 | 7.2 | 1.3 | 1.0 | 8.7 | 22.4 | 21.7 | 5.5 | 7.1 | 4.3 |

*Source:* Same as Table 28.

TABLE 31. SUICIDE RATES PER 100,000 POPULATION

| Area | Total | White | Nonwhite |
|---|---|---|---|
| United States | 10.6 | 11.4 | 4.5 |
| Virginia | 12.1 | 14.0 | 5.1 |
| New England | 9.1 | 9.2 | 6.0 |
| South Atlantic | 11.0 | 13.1 | 3.8 |
| Pacific | 15.2 | 15.9 | 8.1 |

*Source:* L. I. Dublin, *Suicide, a Sociological and Statistical Study* (New York, 1963).

how do we compare with the nation and with some of our neighboring
and other sister states? Figure 6 will give some of the most recent data,
which essentially speak for themselves.

In a recent phamphlet published by the Virginia Association for
Mental Health entitled *Mental Hygiene Clinic: Aftercare in Virginia in
1964* it was dramatically demonstrated how aftercare can affect mental
health conditions in Virginia (Figure 7 is taken from that pamphlet).
The association called aftercare for the mentally ill a "major break-
through in limiting the cost spiral of mental health care." They are
unquestionably correct in this appraisal; on the basis of a controlled study

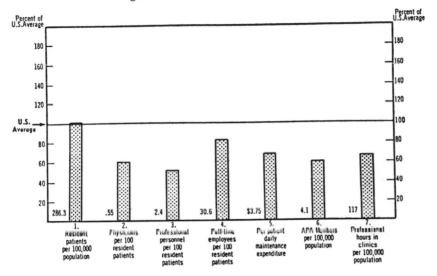

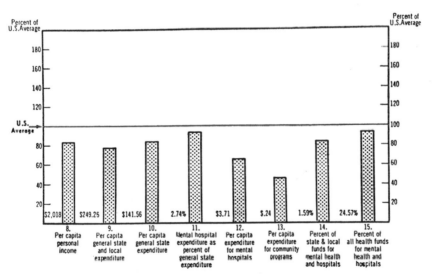

6. *Virginia's standing in relation to the national average in fifteen indices, 1962. (From Joint Information Service of the American Psychiatric Association and the National Association for Mental Health,* Fifteen Indices—An Aid in Reviewing State and Local Mental Health and Hospital Programs, *Washington, 1964.)*

it was demonstrated that aftercare cuts hospital admissions in half and costs only one-tenth as much as hospital care. The clinics are, however, "already overloaded. . . . In order for the localities to embark on the new aftercare activity the localities have every reason to expect the

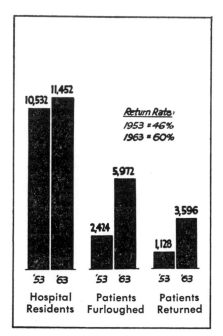

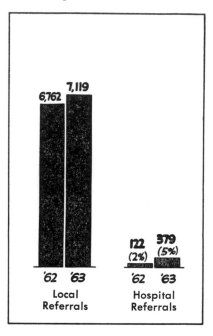

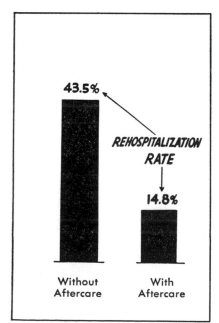

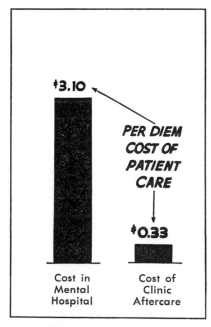

7. *Virginia's experience with rehospitalization and aftercare.* (*From Virginia Association for Mental Health,* Mental Hygiene Clinic Aftercare in Virginia in 1964 [*Richmond, 1964*].)

Commonwealth of Virginia to continue to support its share of the cost of this expanded work."[24]

In an editorial entitled "A Step in the Right Direction" published in the *Virginia Medical Monthly* Dr. James B. Funkhouser and Miss Edna M. Lantz were able to point to improvement in the effectiveness of the state mental hospitals as reflected in "effective release rates." They showed that, of the patient population in all the hospitals residing in rural areas, the effective release rate for 1962–63 was 32.5 compared to the rate in 1960–61 of 29.0. The effective release rate for cities for 1962–63 was 41.51, compared to the 1960–61 rate of 36.3. In summary the authors say:

The encouraging note is that over a three year period, the improvement is significant for all hospitals individually and collectively. Intensified efforts by the department's mental hygiene clinics and the cooperation of local health departments in providing aftercare services for patients re-leased from the hospitals have undoubtedly made a major contribution to this overall improvement. . . . In dollars and cents, this improve-ment in effective release has tremendous importance. The taxpayer pays less for an outpatient than a patient in the hospital—much less, since room, board, laundry, nursing and recreational services are not involved in caring for outpatients. But the greatest contribution is humane. A patient with his family, in most instances working at a job, or at least helping out in the home is a happier one than the patient in a mental hospital.[25]

In the area of service, then, Virginia can take some satisfaction and encouragement in the progress that is being made. Anyone familiar, however, with present conditions and with the tables showing Virginia's relative standing in the provision of mental care services will know that we have a long way to go.

## Professional Manpower in the Mental Health Services

One of the great bottlenecks frustrating attempts to provide more adequate and comprehensive services in the area of mental health is the shortage of trained personnel in all categories. There is a great need for more psychiatrists, psychologists, and psychiatric social workers, and the state should assume responsibility for considerable expansion of the training programs of these and other professional workers. Only the Richmond Professional Institute offers training at the master's level in psychiatric social work and clinical psychology. No graduate work in

[24] (Richmond, 1964), pp. 1–2.
[25] James D. Funkhouser and Edna M. Lantz "A Step in the Right Direction," *Virginia Medical Monthly*, 91 (April 1964), 168–69.

psychiatric nursing is offered in Virginia. The psychiatric work at the two state medical schools and in the state hospitals should be further developed, with the hospitals affiliating their programs with those of the medical schools. Other important ancillary service personnel such as occupational, recreational, and industrial therapists, vocational rehabilitation workers, nurses, and aides are in short supply and totally insufficient to staff the community hospitals and mental health clinics that are needed.

It is well to recall that nationally only 18 percent of those seeking help for psychological or adjustment problems go to psychiatrists or psychologists, whereas 42 percent go first to clergymen and 29 percent to general physicians. We should recognize the tremendous service rendered by these groups and by welfare workers, public health nurses, teachers, and others. The important function of many laymen's organizations such as the local chapters of Mental Health Associations and the Society for Mentally Retarded is also acknowledged.

It is clear that we may never have enough professional mental health workers to meet the problem. Part of the answer lies in training nonprofessional aides and those able to do counseling such as ministers, teachers, welfare workers, and vocational rehabilitation workers.

### Research

Research is significantly listed last, since this is certainly the place it has occupied in Virginia. Perhaps it should have come first, because it may hold the answer, or at least better answers, to all of our problems. Of course, some research is under way, notably at the two medical schools and in departments of psychology elsewhere, but very little of it is supported by the state.

The General Assembly of 1944 authorized the creation of a Virginia Institute of Psychiatry, but no money has ever been appropriated nor any plans formulated for its construction and operation. Such an institute could greatly augment training and research activities and help fulfill the responsibility of the state in these areas. It would also, of course, quickly benefit and upgrade the quality and extent of mental health services.

### Conclusion

The progress made in psychiatry generally during the past ten years has been aptly summarized by Stuart C. Knox, a Los Angeles psychiatrist. Despite our failure to discover the exact "cause" of mental illness, extremely significant and far-reaching developments in treatment have altered an otherwise dismal picture. According to Knox,

During the past ten years, psychiatry has made advances which can be considered nothing short of revolutionary.

It is this change of attitude toward mental illness that has been the revolutionary thing. Developments which have made this possible are the concepts of the plausibility and rationality of drug therapy; of open ward treatment for the vast majority of psychiatric patients; of community-centered treatment programs rather than isolated management in "out of sight, out of mind" locations; of treatment of psychiatric patients in general hospitals where they have the advantage of full medical services while the staff members have the opportunity of following and participating in the progress of their patients during psychiatric treatment; and, finally, of the extensive involvement of the nonpsychiatric physician in the process of treatment of patients with mental disorders.

Today most authorities subscribe to the idea that, for best results in psychiatric problems, adequate treatment must be available as early, as continuously, with as little dislocation, and with as much social restoration as possible. These criteria provide guidelines for all projected trends in the development of treatment patterns to cope with the rising demand for psychiatric help.[26]

Virginia currently falls far short of this ideal for most of its people. It ranks below the national averages in most of the criteria by which standards are set for the quantity and the quality of the services available for the mentally ill. It has made progress; yet it has fallen farther behind. In general, our problems are not different in degree or kind from those of the rest of the nation. Much has been accomplished of which we can be proud, but much more remains to be done.

[26] "A Decade of Progress in Psychiatry," *Journal of the American Medical Association*, 187 (March 21, 1964), 959–60.

# Talents, Intelligence, and Aptitudes in Virginia's Population

*John J. McMillan*

*Formerly Chief Psychologist*

*Department of Psychiatry*

*Medical College of Virginia*

9

In the early years of the United States, Virginia carried more than its proportionate weight of eminence and leadership. Witness the fact that eight American Presidents were born in Virginia, and seven of these were born within a fifty-one-year span in the eighteenth century. Of course, the United States was then smaller geographically, and Virginia was a relatively larger part of the nation than it is at present, but the record stands as an extraordinary chapter in the history of human resources.

This essay is concerned with Virginia in the twentieth century. Its specific interest is with indices of talent, intelligence, and aptitudes in Virginia's population in the 1960's. The goal set is much more modest than may be implied by the title. The purpose here is to look at some selected variables that may indirectly reflect such positive human attributes as talent, intelligence, and aptitudes. These variables are to be examined in terms of general trends rather than extensively and deeply. The conclusions can at best be suggestive and, hopefully, provocative, rather than definitive and comprehensive. In short, this paper will constitute a survey of some other surveys.

Because of the known hazards of misleading information emanating from poorly conceived surveys—especially those touching on such emotionally toned subjects as talent and ability—we have taken pains here to select those surveys that satisfy certain criteria such as representativeness, nonartificiality, and the like.

The following criteria will serve as rough guidelines for our present purposes: (1) Select from already existing surveys of the population that provide state, regional, and national information. (2) Data should reflect natural rather than experimentally controlled conditions. (3) Data should be reasonably representative of the population characteristics in question. (4) Data should permit comparisons by geographical areas and along a temporal dimension, even if a short one.

In connection with the last criterion mentioned, the following comments are in order. Geographical comparisons will be made consistently by state (Virginia), region, and nation. "Region" is here defined as the "South Atlantic Division"[1] (following the lead of the United States

[1] Hereafter often referred to simply as the "region" or by the initials "SAD."

159

Bureau of the Census[2] and the National Science Foundation's report of scientific and technical personnel [1960]) and includes the following: Delaware, Maryland, District of Columbia, Virginia, West Virginia, North Carolina, South Carolina, Georgia, and Florida. In terms of the time dimension, we will restrict ourselves primarily to data collected from 1960 on.

Omitted in this survey are comparative analyses in terms of intrastate, ethnic, class, or religious differences, even though such data would be of great value. (Most surveys that tap variables of interest to the topic at hand do not ordinarily break down their data in these terms, and retrieval of the appropriate information would be very difficult.) Furthermore, there will be no treatment of the effects of movement or mobility of the population on talent and mental ability. The surveys cited, in effect, have caught the population *in situ* on the basis of their stated place of residence at the time of the collection of data. Regrettably, it will not be possible to say anything about the amount of talent importation and exportation that has occurred. Such information, also of great potential value, would either require new surveys expressly designed for this purpose or necessitate a careful and costly extraction of data already collected but not readily available for retrieval.

Despite these restrictions some intriguing mining among the quarries of annual reports and surveys has been carried out, and the results may now be presented. The variables are grouped under the following four general categories:

1. General approximators of mental ability. These include (a) test performance of inductees into the military service and (b) standardized test scores of persons applying for entry into medical schools.

2. Inventiveness. This involves the issuance of patents to individuals or corporations in different localities. This variable, closely related to creativity, should certainly have more detailed treatment than can be given here, but the stated criteria imposed limitations on other appropriate measures of creativity.[3]

3. Scientific and scholarship skills. Here may be found rich sources of data. These include the number and types of scientists as reported by the National Science Foundation, National Merit Scholarship winners, Science Talent Search awardees, and the number and geographical location of Rhodes Scholars.

4. Leadership or eminence. Listings in *Who's Who in America* will constitute the prime variable.

Other variables whetted our investigative appetite but, because of

[2] See *The World Almanac 1964 and Book of Facts,* ed. Harry Hansen (New York, 1964), p. 250.

[3] An informative study of creativity in gifted children is reported in the book *Creativity and Intelligence* (New York, 1962) by J. W. Getzels and P. W. Jackson.

nonrepresentativeness or difficulty of retrieval of pertinent data, had to be abandoned. These included (a) Miller Analogies Test scores—a measure of high levels of abstract thinking ability; (b) College Boards examination scores—unfortunately, data are not readily retrievable according to the student's place of residence; (c) membership in the Young Presidents' Organization[4]—not representative of the population; and (d) Project TALENT data[5]—a potentially rich source of pertinent information being collected by Flanagan's American Institute for Research but one which, by prior agreement with the funding agencies, cannot be identified by state.

## Report of Findings

Before examining specific findings it should be restated that nationally the total number of states will be fifty-one (because the District of Columbia will be included as a "state") and regionally it will be nine, as listed previously. If the 1960 census is used as a reference point, it is helpful to remember that the South Atlantic Division constitutes 14.5 percent of the total population, and Virginia constitutes 15.4 percent of the region's population.[6]

It should also be carefully re-emphasized that the analyses to follow do not attempt to identify or explain the effect of unusual or fortuitous concentrations of skilled manpower within certain geographical boundaries because of the presence therein of large governmental or commercial agencies or installations. The data are presented as originally collected by others and with state lines as the basis for demarcation. The results should emphatically not be construed as necessarily reflecting characteristics of a native or indigenous population.

### Mental Ability Indicators

Performance on a mental test of inductees into the armed services constitutes one basis for comparison. The test in question is the Armed Forces Qualifications Test (AFQT), a test developed jointly by all the military services and consisting of a hundred items equally divided between the four content areas of vocabulary, arithmetic, spatial relation-

---

[4] Young Presidents' Organization, *What Is YPO?* (New York, n.d.).

[5] J. C. Flanagan *et al., The Talents of American Youth, Book 1,* "Design for a Study of American Youth" (New York, 1962).

[6] In making geographical comparisons, data from the next smaller subunit are not excluded, i.e., in referring to national trends we are leaving in the data from the region and in referring to regional trends we are leaving in data from Virginia. Leaving in these data creates some small correlation between the sets of scores, but this is felt to be a minor problem compared to the statistically cumbersome task of excluding such data from already collected and compiled surveys.

ships, and mechanical ability. Examinees are placed in terms of their scores into one of five categories or "mental groups"—with "I" assigned to the highest group and "V" to the lowest. Persons in the latter category fall in the lowest 9 percent of the testing population and are said to have failed the test in terms of not meeting the minimum standards judged necessary for entry into military service.[7] In Figures 8 and 9 may be

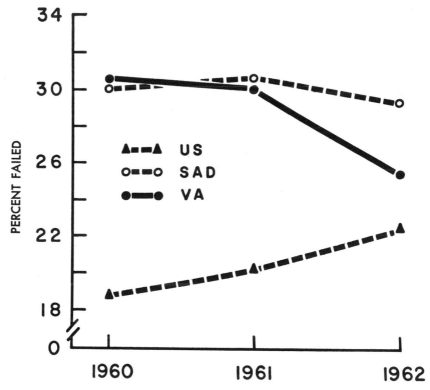

8. *Percentage of men failing mental test (AFQT) for military service.* US = nation; SAD = region (South Atlantic Division); VA = state (Virginia).

found some comparative data on this test. The information is presented in terms of rankings or percentages rather than in absolute numbers.[8]

Figure 8 shows the percentage of examinees who failed the mental test—that is, fell into mental group V—but were physically qualified in

[7] B. D. Karpinos, "Fitness of American Youth for Military Service," *Milbank Memorial Fund Quarterly*, 38 (1960), 213–47.

[8] "Preinduction and Induction Examination Results 1960," *Health of the Army*, 15 (1960), 1–10; "Results of the Examination of Youths for Military Service 1961," *ibid.*, 17 (1962, no. 2), 1–17; "Results of the Examination of Youths for Military Service 1962," *ibid.* (no. 10), 1–20.

the years 1960, 1961, and 1962. The data are given in terms of the state of Virginia, the SAD and the United States as a whole. It is apparent from this graph that Virginia and the region fared less well than did the nation as a whole. It is noteworthy, however, that whereas the national averages show a slight progressive increase in the percentage of failures

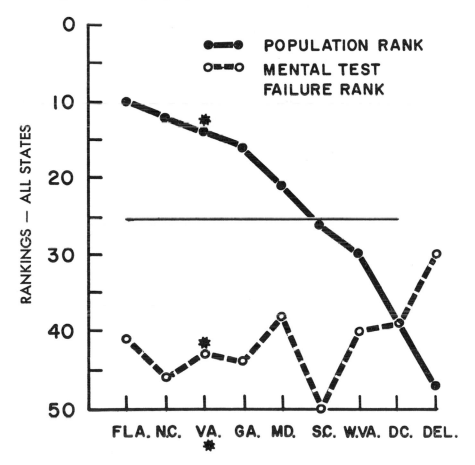

9. *Population (1960 figures) vs. mental test failures, rankings of South Atlantic Division states. Virginia rankings are emphasized by asterisks. The horizontal center line represents median rank for all states and the District of Columbia.*

on the test from 1960 to 1962, Virginia shows a progressive decrease in percentage of failures, and the regional values remain about the same. This is obviously too short a time span to be interpreted as a meaningful or stable trend.

Figure 9 shows how the various states within SAD rank among

themselves and against the national rankings in terms of the percentage of inductees failing the mental test for the year 1960. The eight states and the District of Columbia are arranged along the horizontal axis in terms of their decreasing populations. The vertical axis indicates their rankings from high (at the top) to low (at the bottom). The horizontal line drawn at the center represents the mid-point in the rankings of the fifty states and the District. This graph yields a somewhat more disturbing representation of what was pictured in Figure 1, for it is apparent that, except for Delaware, the states of the region fall within the bottom fourth of all the states in terms of failing the mental test. Virginia, for instance, ranks forty-third, with a percentage of failure of about 31 (see again Figure 8). The range of failures was from a low of 3.4 percent for Montana to a high of 50.9 percent for Mississippi. The national average that year was 18.8 percent (see Figure 8). Since these findings refer to a young adult male population that excludes those potentially deferrable for entry into college—for which other standardized tests are available—we are probably sampling here, not the whole range of mental ability, but the lower portion particularly.

The Medical College Admissions Test (MCAT) is a widely employed test which, though developed as one of the selection tools for admission to medical schools, also measures to some extent general mental ability as well as the more specific aptitudes pertinent to a medical education. It is useful here because it taps a relatively well-represented component of our general population—that is, young persons who aspire to become physicians. Statistical analyses for the academic year 1960–61 from the American Association of Medical Colleges suggest, for example, that the tendency to apply for medical school is—per capita—relatively uniform

TABLE 32. FREQUENCY DISTRIBUTION OF APPLICANTS FOR MEDICAL SCHOOL PER 100,000 STATE POPULATION, 1960–61

| Class interval Applicants/100,000 | | Frequencies National | SAD |
|:---:|:---:|:---:|:---:|
| 14–15 | | 1 | 1 |
| 12–13 | | 2 | 0 |
| 10–11 | | 3 | 0 |
| 8–9 | | 22 | 5 |
| 6–7 | | 17 | 2 |
| 4–5 | | 5 | 1 |
| 2–3 | | 1 | 0 |
| | Totals | 51 | 9 |

Virginia's applicant rate is 6.28 per 100,000 population.

from state to state and that regional characteristics closely parallel national trends (see Table 32).[9]

This nationally standardized test measures the students' abilities in four general areas: verbal comprehension, concepts of quantity, knowledge of modern society, and grasp of science. Of these four, the verbal portion is probably most closely associated with general intellectual ability. As with many other nationally standardized achievement or aptitude tests, the MCAT scores are based on a mean of 500 and a standard deviation of 100.

Figure 10 provides comparative data on the MCAT scores of appli-

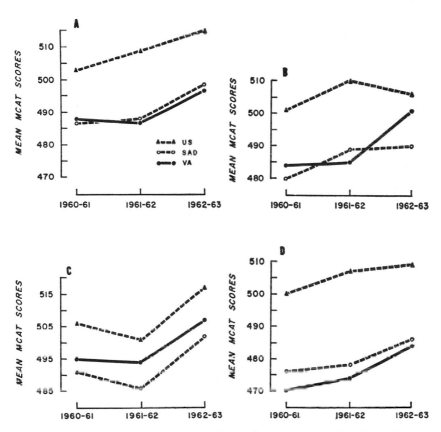

*10. Performance on Medical College Admissions Test (MCAT), by nation, region, and state for three academic years, 1960–61, 1961–62, and 1962–63. A, scores on verbal portion of test; B, scores on quantitative portion; C, scores on modern society portion; D, scores on science portion.*

[9] E. B. Hutchins and Helen H. Gee, "The Study of Applicants," *J. Med. Educ.,* 37 (1962), 1203–12.

cants for each of the four component parts of the test for three academic-year periods.[10] In Figure 10-A are data on the verbal portion of the MCAT for geographical areas. It may be observed that the national average tends to stay about 0.2 of a standard deviation above the regional and state means and that there is also a general but slight improvement in average scores from year to year. Virginia's mean scores show virtually no difference from the region's from year to year. Figure 10-B provides comparable information for the quantitative section of the MCAT. The national averages are consistently above the regional and state levels, although Virginia's mean shows a fairly striking rise toward the national average for the academic year 1962–63. In Figure 10-C Virginia is consistently above the average for the region though below the national average on the modern society portion of the MCAT. Figure 10-D gives data on the science portion of the MCAT. Here the gap between regional and state figures, on one hand, and the national trend, on the other, is most striking and should probably be the source of most concern, especially since the Virginia averages fall consistently if only slightly below the regional means.

Figure 11 provides a composite picture of the four parts of Figure 10,

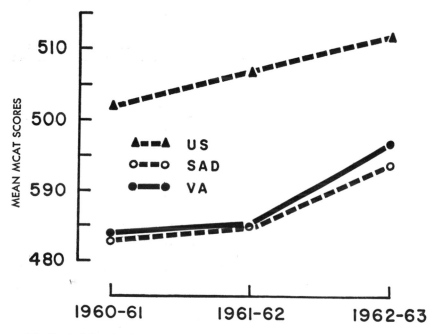

*11. Pooled Medical College Admissions Test scores, by nation, region, and state, for 1960–61, 1961–62, and 1962–63.*

[10] E. B. Hutchins, "The Study of Applicants, 1961–62," and "The Study of Applicants," *J. Med. Educ.*, 38 (1963), 707–17, 999–1003.

the separate sections of the MCAT having been pooled in terms of an over-all mean. The lines here are strikingly similar to those of Figure 10-A, which measured verbal ability, and generally show Virginia as about equal to the average of the region but with both nearly 0.2 of a standard deviation below the national average. It is encouraging to note, however, that over-all performances on the MCAT are showing a slight rise, both nationally and locally.[11]

### Inventiveness

Although there is much interest these days in identifying and assessing creativity, no systematic or representative samplings of this attribute in the population could be located. One intriguing and possibly significant index is the extent to which individuals or corporations apply for and are awarded patents for inventions. Certainly inventiveness and creativity have something in common. The patent office of the United States Department of Commerce publishes annual reports of the granting of patents by geographical area, and pertinent information is presented herewith.[12]

Figure 12 provides some revealing data for the years 1960, 1961, and 1962. The rankings of the states of the South Atlantic Division are plotted against those of the states as a whole. The nine SAD states are separately identified. Rankings here are based on the number of patents issued in relation to the population of each of the states for each year. These rankings are based on a lumping of patents issued to individuals and corporations. Thus Delaware, which ranks first both regionally and nationally, was issued the most patents in relation to its population. (The du Pont complex in Wilmington is obviously an important if not a key factor in this finding.) It can be seen that West Virginia shows a slight progressive improvement in relative position, whereas most of the other states hold relatively unchanging rankings.[13]

### Scientific and Scholarship Skills

One reasonable index of talents, intelligence, and aptitudes is the number and types of scientists distributed throughout the population. A ready source of data is the periodic report on American scientific

[11] MCAT score data for the South Atlantic Division were kindly furnished by Dr. E. B. Hutchins of the Basic Research Division, American Association of Medical Colleges. Previous publications had not grouped the data in this way, as the AAMC employs a different basis for regional comparisons.

[12] U.S. Department of Commerce, Patent Office, *Patents Issued to Residents of United States, Puerto Rico, and Other Areas under the American Flag* (Annual reports for calendar years 1960, 1961, 1962; Washington, D.C., n.d.).

[13] The author is indebted to Mr. Isaac Fleischmann, director of the Office of Information Services of the Patent Office, for furnishing the reports containing data on which this section of the paper has been based.

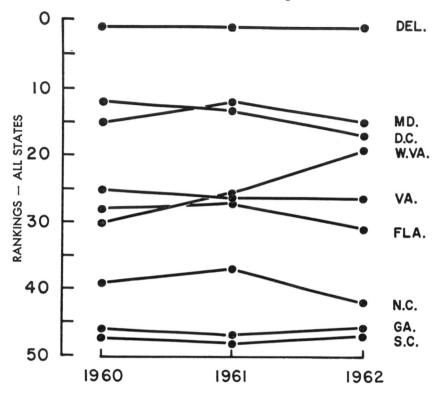

*12. Patents awarded, rankings of South Atlantic Division states in relation to population. Rankings are based on all patents, whether to individuals or corporations.*

manpower growing out of the National Science Foundation's (NSF's) National Register of Scientific and Technical Personnel. The last detailed report was published in 1960, and three brief but fact-filled *Scientific Manpower Bulletins* have been issued since.[14] Based on questionnaires sent to all members of the national associations of the major scientific disciplines, these reports provide data on scientists in a wide range of areas including foreign language competence, specialty skills, salaries, major duties, and the like. Of interest here is how these scientists are distributed in the population.

Figure 13 provides regional data for the year 1960 on the ranking of the states in terms of the number of scientists in each state compared to the population. The solid line shows the relative rankings of the SAD states in terms of population. The dotted line shows the rankings of the SAD states in terms of number of scientists. Where the dotted line falls

[14] Nos. 18, 19, 20; Nov. and Dec. 1962 and March 1964.

below the solid line, one can infer a relative deficit of scientists per total population; where it rises above the solid line, one can infer an above-average proportion of scientists. The distance of the dotted line below or above the solid line gives an indication, albeit somewhat general, of the degree of relative deficit or surplus. From Figure 13 it is plain that six of the regional states, including Virginia, are in the deficit category, whereas Delaware, the District of Columbia, and Maryland are strikingly high in the surplus category. West Virginia, by this index of comparative rankings, comes closest to having a balance between population and number of scientists. It should be noted that the figures for Maryland, Virginia, and the District of Columbia are affected by the concentration

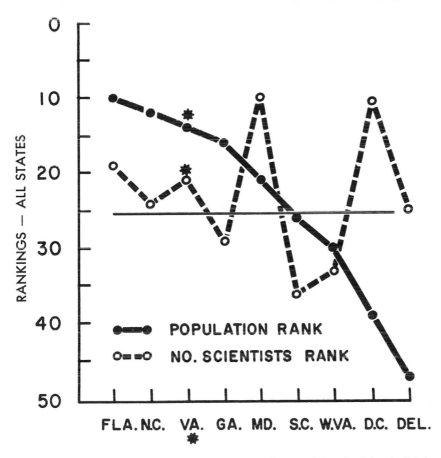

13. *Population vs. number of scientists, rankings of South Atlantic Division states. The 1960 figures are from the National Science Foundation. The horizontal center line represents the median rank for all states and the District of Columbia.*

of scientific facilities and installations around the "greater Washington" area. Delaware also presents a somewhat unique situation in that, while a small state in terms of total population, it cradles the central core of the far-flung du Pont interests in the city of Wilmington.

Figure 14 gives a picture of the relative number of different types of scientists according to geographical location. These data are again presented in terms of national, regional, and Virginia percentages. (Also included in this figure are absolute numbers in order to provide some picture of the scientific manpower resources.) This graphic portrayal is interesting in that the three lines so closely parallel each other. That is to say, even though the region as a whole and Virginia as a state show a generalized relative deficit in number of scientists, the representation of different types of scientists and technical personnel shows a close congruence with the national picture. Stated another way, the state may not have enough scientists but it does have a typical distribution of types. Note again that these data do not identify the type, size, or specific location of the institutions where the scientists are employed.

Let us now see how the different geographical areas fare in terms of the performance of high school students applying for the Westinghouse Science Scholarships and Awards as part of the Annual Science Talent Search. Sponsored by the Science Clubs of America and now in its twenty-third year, this program publishes annual reports on the honors groups and the winners. The honors group consists of those who fall in the top 10 percent of the students who complete entries in the Science Talent Search, and the winners are a select and fixed number chosen from the honors group. Different states have reportedly shown some variation in both the timing and extent of involvement in this program, and there may be some question as to whether indices drawn from this source constitute adequately representative samples of scientific talent or potential. One mimeographed report produced by Science Service, Washington, D.C., in January 1962, provides data over a twenty-two-year span—from 1942 through 1963—in terms of the standings of the states (including Alaska, Hawaii, and the District of Columbia) as regards the number of students in (a) the honors group and (b) the winners.[15]

In Figure 15—using the 1960 population figures as a reference point—are comparisons, made with some caution and misgivings, of the rankings of the states of the region in terms of population versus their rankings in producing (cumulatively over the twenty-two-year span) Science Talent Search winners and honors awardees. Figure 15 suggests that, as a region, the states fall below the national average since the

[15] "Standing of the States in the Annual Science Talent Search for the Westinghouse Science Scholarships and Awards: 1942–1963, Honors Group and Winners" (Washington, D.C., 1963), mimeo.

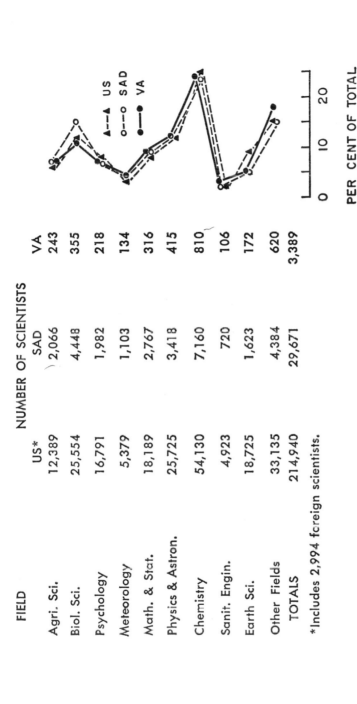

NUMBER OF SCIENTISTS

| FIELD | US* | SAD | VA |
|---|---|---|---|
| Agri. Sci. | 12,389 | 2,066 | 243 |
| Biol. Sci. | 25,554 | 4,448 | 355 |
| Psychology | 16,791 | 1,982 | 218 |
| Meteorology | 5,379 | 1,103 | 134 |
| Math. & Stat. | 18,189 | 2,767 | 316 |
| Physics & Astron. | 25,725 | 3,418 | 415 |
| Chemistry | 54,130 | 7,160 | 810 |
| Sanit. Engin. | 4,923 | 720 | 106 |
| Earth Sci. | 18,725 | 1,623 | 172 |
| Other Fields | 33,135 | 4,384 | 620 |
| TOTALS | 214,940 | 29,671 | 3,389 |

*Includes 2,994 foreign scientists.

PER CENT OF TOTAL

14. Percentage of scientific specialties, by nation, region, and state. Absolute values are shown for each specialty in the three columns to the left of the percentages. (Data from NSF, Scientific Manpower Bulletin. No. 20, March 1964.)

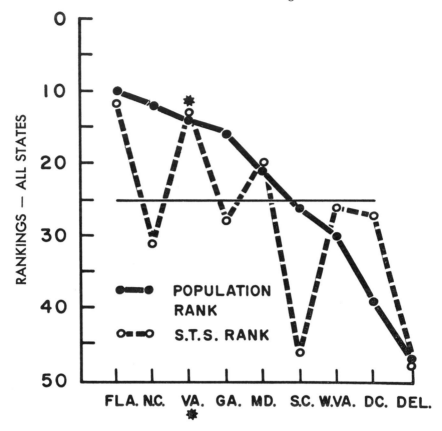

15. *Population (1960 figures) vs. high scores in Science Talent Search, rankings of South Atlantic Division states. See text for further explanation.*

dotted line is predominantly below the solid line representing relative population size. Except for "poor showings" by South Carolina, North Carolina, and Georgia, which contribute heavily to this appearance of deficit, however, the other states of SAD do fairly well on this index. Virginia, it can be seen, contributes slightly more than its share in terms of population size. The District shows the highest "overage."

A related index of scholarship talent among students is the National Merit Scholarship Program, which annually awards scholarships to promising high-school seniors entering college. The final awards are allocated on the basis of the population in each state (and in four re-gions) in order to represent the population of the nation as a whole. This allocation has the effect of masking, to some extent, the absolute differences in ability as determined by the scores on the National Merit Scholarship Qualifying Test (NMSQT).

Of some usefulness, however, is the minimum qualifying score set for candidates in each state. This score, although in some ways a crude measure for our purposes, probably correlates quite well with the mean score for each state.[16] The NMSQT is a three-hour test of educational development and readiness for college which, according to the 1963 NMSP guide booklet, is designed to measure "both aptitude and attainment . . . [and] to discover those bright students who have applied their abilities."[17] The NMSQT is composed of five subtests—English usage, social studies reading, natural sciences reading, mathematics usage, and word usage. The qualifying score is based on the totals of the examinee's standard scores on each of the five subtests.

In Figure 16 can be seen comparative data for mean qualifying scores

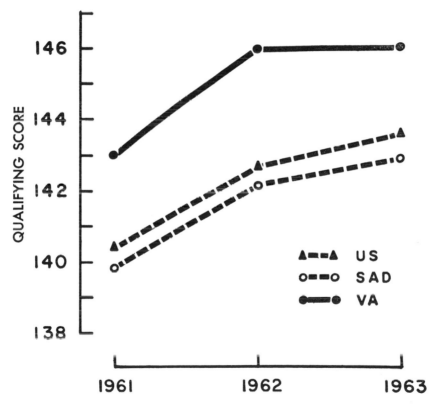

16. *Qualifying scores on National Merit Scholarship Qualification Test (NMSQT), by nation, region, and state. National and regional values are represented by mean qualifying scores.*

[16] Alexander W. Astin, research associate, National Merit Scholarship Corporation, personal communication.

[17] National Merit Scholarship Corporation, *Guide to the National Merit Scholarship Program* (Annual guides for 1961, 1962, 1963; Evanston, Ill., n.d.), p. 10.

on the NMSQT for the years 1961, 1962, and 1963. The range of qualifying scores from state to state is not great (for instance, it was only 137 to 149 in 1963), and therefore this may be a relatively insensitive measure. The data are presented here purely for their suggestive value. Virginia shows up rather well, with its qualifying score falling consistently above the regional and national averages. Again we note a phenomenon observable in previously cited reports, and that is of an upward trend with succeeding years.

Rhodes Scholarships have also been examined as an index of the distribution of academic talent in the population.[18] Used here is the present residence of all Rhodes Scholars living in the United States rather than their place of residence at the time of application, since the latter information is based on the location of the college or university from which they applied and this may or may not have been in their home state. Even though their present location could be criticized as a misleading indicator—certainly of their origins—it does at least give a picture of where these highly screened and promising scholars have subsequently chosen to live and work.

Figure 17 provides graphic evidence on the comparative rankings of states with regard to the residences of Rhodes Scholars. It can be seen that both the region and the state of Virginia show an over-all clear surplus rather than a deficit. The overcontribution is especially noticeable for the District of Columbia and Delaware.

### Leadership or Eminence

A logical source for an inquiry into this topic is *Who's Who in America,* the well-known biographical dictionary of the notable living men and women of the United States. This biennially appearing volume does not contain a breakdown of its membership by geographical location. However, for a number of years the publishers—Marquis— Who's Who, Inc.—have issued a booklet which does give the geographical locations of the new additions to *Who's Who* membership. Because tallying up membership totals by state loomed as a much too formidable task, it was decided to look for geographic trends in terms of accrued new listings for the last three volumes of *Who's Who in America—* Volume 31 (1958–59) through Volume 33 (1964–65). In this manner it was possible to determine the total new listings for each of the fifty states plus the District of Columbia for an approximate six-year period. A word should be said about the problem of representativeness. The latest volume of *Who's Who* gives the two standards for inclusion of

18 "Addresses and Occupations of Rhodes Scholars and Other Oxonians," *American Oxonian,* 50 (1963, no. 4, pt. 2).

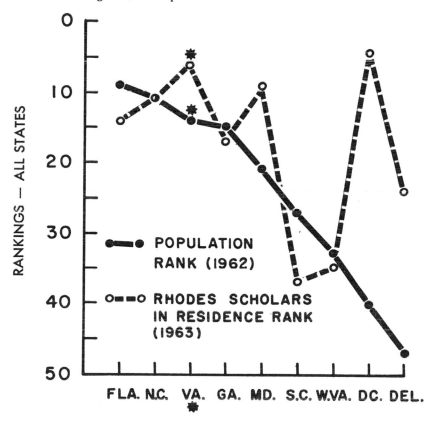

17. *Population (1962 estimated figures) vs. Rhodes Scholars in residence, rankings of South Atlantic Division states (1963 figures).*

members: Group One—those persons who have accomplished some conspicuous achievement; and Group Two—those persons who are "included on account of position—civil, military, religious, educational, corporate or organizational." It is pointed out further that many persons qualified under Group Two would readily satisfy the requirements for Group One.[19] It would seem reasonable that these two criteria, if taken seriously, would not result in unreasonable bias in terms of geographical factors. There is, of course, one obvious exception, and that is the District of Columbia, which, as the seat of the Federal government, can be expected to have an inordinately high representation of members in Group Two.

For purposes of this analysis, the fifty states and the District of Columbia were rank-ordered in terms of accrued new listings for the past

[19] *Who's Who in America, 1964–65* (Chicago, 1964), XXXIII, 2.

six years based on the stated place of residence of each member. As an
added check on the matter of representativeness, a rank-order correlation
(*rho*) was run between the *Who's Who* totals over six years and the total
population for each state for 1960. Even with the District included, a *rho*
of 0.88 was obtained, suggesting a fairly high parallelism between these
two variables for the states. The District was then excluded in another
rank-order correlation between the fifty states, and a *rho* of 0.96 was
obtained, a high correlation indeed. With this in mind Figure 18

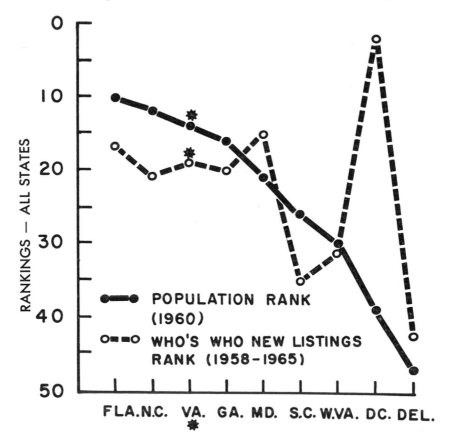

*18. Population (1960 figures) vs. new listings in* Who's Who in America,
*rankings of South Atlantic Division states.*

provides graphic evidence of how Virginia and the other South Atlantic
Division states rank on the *Who's Who* index of eminence. The solid line
ranks the states by population (using 1960 census figures), the dotted
line ranks the SAD states in terms of accrued new listings for *Who's Who
in America*. The District of Columbia's high contribution to the emi-

nence index can be readily seen inasmuch as the District ranks second on this index while ranking thirty-ninth in population. The situation of the other states can also be easily determined from this graph. Six of the remaining eight SAD states have slight deficits on the leadership index, while two—Maryland and Delaware—have slight overages. Except for the District, however, none of these population versus eminence discrepancies is great, and this helps explain the high rank-order correlation between these two variables.

## Discussion and Summary Remarks

The data presented in these findings must, of course, be interpreted with considerable caution and care. Certain observations, however, can be made.

1. The South Atlantic Division states as a group parallel national characteristics on most of the selected indices of talent, intelligence, and aptitudes, although the average level regionally is somewhat below the national average.

2. Intraregional differences are striking in some of the variables selected for study. Maryland, the District of Columbia, and Delaware typically form a strong group within the region, whereas North Carolina, South Carolina, and Georgia typically occupy lower positions in the rankings.

3. Virginia typically falls close to the middle values of the region. This is also generally true of West Virginia and Florida in terms of the variables selected for presentation here.

4. Looking more closely at the results from Virginia, we find some rather interesting possibilities to consider. In our opinion these would warrant further study. In measures of human ability based on general population characteristics Virginia tends to rank below national averages. But in measures reflective of upper levels of ability and eminence Virginia tends to show more favorable rankings. It will be remembered that it exceeded national averages on such indicators as Rhodes Scholars in residence, Science Talent Search winners, and Merit Scholarship scores. These findings suggest that the distribution of ability in the population of Virginia does not precisely match the over-all national pattern. The frequency distribution appears flatter in Virginia than in the nation as a whole. Or, put differently, Virginia appears to have relatively less representation in the broad middle ranges of the spectra of abilities. The implications of this finding are fairly obvious for future educational and vocational planning for the broad middle-class portions of the population.

In conclusion, an attempt is made to present the findings of this essay in tabular rather than in graphic form. Table 33 summarizes the rank discrepancies for those variables presented above in the figures for the separate states in SAD. "Undercontribution" is defined as the extent to which the state ranks lower in the variable in question in relation to its population and "overcontribution" the extent to which it ranks higher. Thus it can be seen that the region as a whole has a mean rank discrepancy of −2.9 in relation to the nation as a whole. In the column

TABLE 33. Six Measures of Ability vs. Population, Rank Discrepancies of South Atlantic Division States in Terms of "Undercontribution" or "Overcontribution"

| SAD States* | AFQT | Patents ('61) | Scientists (NSF) | STS† | WWA‡ | RS§ | ΣD | M | Rank |
|---|---|---|---|---|---|---|---|---|---|
| Florida | −31 | − 2 | − 9 | − 2 | − 7 | − 5 | − 56 | − 9.3 | 6 |
| N. Car. | −34 | −12 | −14 | −19 | − 9 | 0 | − 88 | −14.7 | 7 |
| Virginia | −29 | − 1 | − 7 | + 1 | − 5 | + 8 | − 33 | − 5.5 | 5 |
| Georgia | −38 | −22 | −13 | −12 | − 4 | − 2 | − 91 | −15.2 | 8 |
| Maryland | −27 | +13 | +11 | + 1 | + 6 | +12 | + 16 | + 2.7 | 3 |
| S. Car. | −24 | −23 | −10 | −20 | − 9 | −10 | − 96 | −16.0 | 9 |
| W. Virginia | −10 | 0 | − 3 | + 4 | − 1 | − 2 | − 12 | − 2.0 | 4 |
| D.C. | 0 | +12 | +28 | +12 | +37 | +36 | +125 | +20.8 | 1 |
| Delaware | +17 | +14 | +22 | − 1 | + 4 | +23 | + 79 | +13.2 | 2 |
| ΣD | −176 | −21 | + 5 | −36 | +12 | +60 | −156 | | |
| M | − 19.6 | − 2.3 | + .6 | − 4.0 | + 1.3 | + 6.7 | | − 2.9‖ | |

* Ranked according to population (1960 census).
† Science Talent Search Performance.
‡ *Who's Who in America.*
§ Residence of Rhodes Scholars (1963).
‖ Discrepancy index for region (SAD) vs. national values.

farthest right in this table can be seen the relative rankings of the SAD states in terms of this discrepancy index, a rank of 1 being the most favorable.

This "survey of some other surveys" has been selective and suggestive rather than comprehensive and definitive. It has raised more questions than it has answered, and this is frankly its intent. Many important factors—such as intrastate subregional differences, factors of mobility of population, ethnic and class variables, unusual concentrations of manpower—have not been touched on here but should certainly warrant systematic exploration in the future.

# Index